CHINA BASICS SERIES

CHINA'S GEOGRAPHY

Natural Conditions, Regional Economies, Cultural Features

Author: Zheng Ping   Translator: Chen Gengtao

CHINA INTERCONTINENTAL PRESS

中国基本情况丛书

顾　　问	李　冰　　赵少华	
主　　编	金　晖	
副 主 编	郭长建　　王庆存	
编　　委	宋坚之(执行)　　吴　伟	
编　　辑	杨季明　　张　宏　　潘仙英	
装帧设计	宁成春(特约)　　田　林	

本册责任编辑　　冯凌宇

图书在版编目(CIP)数据

中国地理：自然·经济·人文：英文 / 郑平著.

北京：五洲传播出版社，1998.12

ISBN 7-80113-481-8

Ⅰ.中…

Ⅱ.郑…

Ⅲ.地理-中国-英文

Ⅳ.K92

五洲传播出版社出版发行

北京北三环中路31号　邮政编码 100088

HTTP：//WWW.CICC.ORG.CN

*

利丰雅高印刷(深圳)有限公司印刷

1999年6月第1版　第1次印刷

889×1194毫米 32开 5.5印张 50千字

(005400)

Table of Contents

CHINA

Chapter I

An Outline Geography of China

The People's Republic of China is a vast country with rich natural resources. The Pacific Ocean and the South China Sea lap its shores, and great mountains and rivers adorn its territory. Superior natural conditions provide not only a vast room of subsistence for the Chinese nation but also a strong material foundation for China's social progress.

China is one of the important birthplaces of ancient human beings. More than one million years ago ancestors of the Chinese nation began a primitive social life on this vast land. More than 10 sites of primitive men have been discovered in the reaches of the Yangtze and the Yellow River. They include Yunnan's Yuanmei Man who lived about 1.7 million years ago, Shaanxi's Lantian Man of 800,000 years ago, and the Peking Man of 600,000 years ago.

The Chinese civilization is one of the earliest in the world: it has a recorded history of more than 5,000 years. Chinese agriculture and handicraft industry were among the most developed in the world in history. Chinese culture not only is rich and splendid but also has strong vitality. Among the best-known cultural attainments and pursuits of the Chinese people are silk, pottery-and-porcelain making, architecture, gardening, stone caves, stone engraving, traditional Chinese medicine, wushu (martial arts) and ancient books and records. Many ancient construction projects, which are a crystallization of the wisdom and strength of the Chinese people, have become part of the cultural heritage of the nation. Such projects include the Great Wall, the Grand Canal, an ancient plank road built along the face of cliffs in Sichuan Province, the Dujiang Water Diversion Project in the same province, the Lingqu Canal in Guangxi and the karez -- an irrigation system of wells connected by underground channels used in the central Asian region of Xinjiang.

Places of historical interest, scenic areas and nature reserves for the protection of rare animal and plant species -- these are important heritages left behind by past generations and nature; they are also important conditions for the development of a tourist industry and scientific research. In China at present, with fast economic development

Spring has come to Tianshan Mountains.

propelled by the policies of reform and opening to the outside world, tourist resources are being developed on a massive scale. A total of 119 areas have been designated as state-level places of scenic beauty and/or historical interest, including 19 that have been listed as World Cultural and Natural Heritage sites by the United Nations. Through a recent national poll, the following have been recognized as the Top Ten Places of Scenic Beauty and/or Historical Interest in China: the Great Wall, the Forbidden City in Beijing, Mount Huangshan in Anhui, the West Lake in Hangzhou, Guilin landscape, the Three Gorges of the Yangtze, gardens in Suzhou, the Terra-Cotta Soldiers and Horses of Emperor Qin Shihuang in Xi'an, the Summer Resort of Chengde and the Sun and Moon Lake in Taiwan. Mao Zedong said in one of his poems: "Our motherland is so rich in beauty." This is a most concise summation of China's geographical features.

1.1 Location of the Land

Daytime can be as long as 17 hours in summer near Muhe, Heilongjiang Province, the northernmost city in China.

With 9.6 million square kilometers in land area, China is the third largest country in the world, after Russia and Canada. Besides, it has a sea area of more than 4.7 million square kilometers that lies off the coasts of east and south China.

China is located in the northern hemisphere with all its territories (including marine areas and islands) lying north of the equator. Latitudinally, the southernmost part of the country is the Zengmu Shoal of Hainan province located at latitude 3°58' north ; and its northernmost part touches the central line of the main navigational channel of the Heilongjiang River, at latitude 53°31'10" north; between the two is a distance of 5,500 kilometers. Longitudinally, the westernmost part of the country is the Pamirs west of Wuqia County in the Xinjiang Uygur Autonomous Region located at longitude 73°22'30" east; and its easternmost part is where the Heilongjiang River meets the Wusuli River in Fuyuan County in Heilongjiang Province, at longitude 135°2'30" east; between the two is a distance of 5,200 kilometers. In area, China is almost equal to more than 30 European countries combined. It makes up one quarter of the total area of Asia and one-fifteenth of the total land area of the globe.

China's land border has a total length of more than 20,000 kilometers. Starting from the mouth of the Yalu River, China borders, in a counter-clockwise order, the following 15 countries: Korea, Russia, Mongolia, Kazakhstan, Kyrgyzstan,

Tajikistan, Afghanistan, Pakistan, India, Nepal, Sikkim, Bhutan, Myanmar, Laos and Vietnam. The Chinese mainland is lapped by the Bohai Sea, the Yellow Sea and the East China Sea in the east and by the South China Sea in the south. Across the seas, it faces Japan, the Philippines, Malaysia, Indonesia and Brunei.

The Pamirs in western China

China has a coastline of more than 18,000 kilometers that stretches from the mouth of the Yalu River in the north to the mouth of the Beilun River in the south. The coastline is shaped like a new moon with its back jutting out to the sea. The entire coastline can be divided into two types: the

Facing the sea in the east and south, China has a long coastline.

Nansha Islands, the southernmost Chinese territory, are located near the equator.

hilly-stone type south of the Hangzhou Bay and the plain-sandy type north of it. The winding hilly coastline creates many fine natural harbors which, being ice-free all the year round, are fit for navigation four seasons of the year. This provides good geographical conditions for the construction of ports. The plain-sandy coastline is flat and relatively dry. Areas with sandy beaches are fit for the development of tourism, whereas those with clay beaches are good for entrapping sea water for the production of salt, thereby providing an inexhaustible raw material for the development of the chemical industry.

Off the coast of China are scattered more than 6,000 islands and islets with a total area of 80,000 square kilometers. The biggest among them is the 36,000-square-kilometer Taiwan Island and the second biggest, the 34,000-square-kilometer Hainan Island. These two have always been known as China's "treasure islands," beautiful and richly endowed. Diaoyu Island and Chiwei Islet located in a sea area to the northeast of Taiwan Island are China's easternmost islands. The more than 200 islands, reefs, shoals and cays scattered in the vast South China Sea belong to Dongsha, Xisha, Zhongsha and Nansha islands. They are collectively called the South China Sea Islands. Other important archipelagos are Miaodao, Changshan, Zhoushan and Penghu. The Zhoushan Archipelago off the coast of Zhejiang Province is a tourist resort: Mount Putuo on its main island is a Buddhist shrine. Around the archipelago is also the vast Zhoushan Fishing Ground known far and wide for its rich fish resources and the high quality of the fish. That is why the Zhoushan Archipelago is also known as "a Buddhist kingdom on the sea" and "the fish storehouse in the orient." Since antiquity, all these islands have been part of China's sacred territory. They are expected to play an increasingly important role in China's economic development.

Location of China in the World

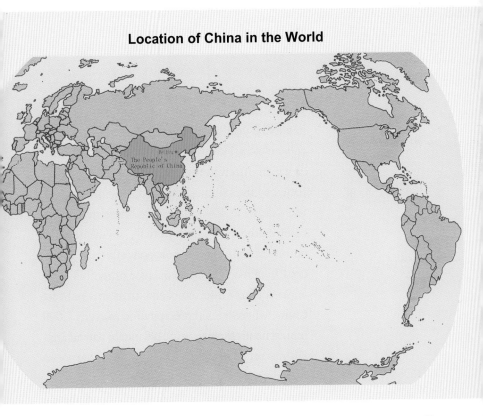

1.2
Geographical Features

China has superior natural conditions, as is evident in its climate and topography.

It is one of the countries that straddle the greatest number of climatic zones. From north to south, the country covers six climatic zones: frigid-temperate, temperate, warm-temperate, subtropical, tropical and equatorial. That is to say, China has all the earth's climatic zones except tundra and permafrost zones that are located close to the polar region. It is worth mentioning that the bulk of the Chinese territory is in the temperate, warm-temperate and subtropical zones. A warm climate with distinct four seasons makes the country an ideal place for mankind to live and develop.

The vastness of the country brings about great regional differences in precipitation. For many years, China's annual precipitation averages 629 mm and a year's total rainfall exceeds six trillion cubic meters. However, owing to different degrees to which different regions of the country are affected by the summer monsoon, precipitation differs sharply in different regions, the general trend being a progressive drop from the southeast to the northwest. With strong monsoon influence, southern China receives an abundance of rainfall. This is particularly true in coastal areas in southeast China, where annual precipitation exceeds 1,000 mm. A national record of 8,408 mm of annual rainfall was set up in the Huoshaoliao area at the northeastern tip of Taiwan. Rainfall is scarce in northwest China located in the heart of Eurasia where the summer monsoon has little influence. Except for a few high mountains, the bulk of the area that receives less than 200 mm of precipitation a year, is desert and semi-desert. Annual precipitation in Ruoqiang area in the heart of the Taklimakan Desert in Xinjiang is as little as less than 10 mm to become the driest place in China.

The east Asian monsoon has a far-reaching influence over climate in China. In summer, when a southeastern wind dominates, the weather becomes hot and rainy with temperatures higher than those in other countries of the same latitudes. In winter, when a northern wind holds sway, it becomes cold and dry with temperatures lower than those in other

A village in northeast China

countries of the same latitudes. High temperatures in summer allow people in vast areas in north China to grow rice, cotton and other heat-loving plants; furthermore, heat is usually accompanied by plenty of rainfall, providing good conditions for the growth of summer crops.

China's landform is varied, encompassing mountains, plateaus, basins, plains and hilly areas. Each type of landform presents a particular natural landscape. China is a mountainous country: mountains, plateaus and hilly areas make up about 65% of its total land area. Many tall and long mountain ranges constitute the framework of the country's landform. They crisscross one another

The Pearl River Delta in Guangdong Province, south China

Hainan Island in the South China Sea

to form geographical "networks" which, encompassing plateaus, plains and basins of different shapes and sizes, present different landforms.

The Chinese landmass descends in height from west to east, dropping in a stair fashion. From low to high elevations, the country can be divided into three stairs. The first stair lies east of a straight line stretching from the Greater Hinggan Mountains in northeast China to the Taihang-Wushan-Xuefeng ranges in the south.

On this stair are mostly plains and hilly areas less than 500 meters above sea level, including the country's three great plains -- the Northeast China Plain, the North China Plain and the Plain of the Middle and Lower Reaches of the Yangtze River -- as well as its largest hilly area, the Southeast China Hilly Land.

The second stair lies west of a straight line from the Greater Hinggan Mountains to the Taihang-Wushan-Xuefeng ranges. On this stair are plateaus and basins with elevations ranging from 1,000 to 2,000 meters above sea level, including three of China's four plateaus -- the Inner Mongolia Plateau, the Loess Plateau and the Yunnan-Guizhou Plateau, and its four great basins -- the Sichuan Basin, the Tarim Basin, the Junggar Basin and the Qaidam Basin.

The third stair is the Qinghai-Tibet Plateau consisting of highlands and mountain ranges with elevations of 4,000 meters and 5,000-6,000 meters above sea level respectively. Along the ranges are scattered more than 10 peaks of more than 8,000 meters above sea level. Mount Qomolangma of the Himalayas along the Chinese-Nepalese border has a height of 8,848.13 meters above sea level, the tallest peak in the world. That is why the Qinghai-Tibet Plateau is also known as "the roof of the world."

This sloping topography allows humid air currents above the sea to penetrate deep into China's interior areas; at the same time, big rivers flow invariably eastward into the sea as transportation arteries between inland and coastal areas, and their big flow drops contain huge hydropower resources. Taking advantage of its topography, China has built numerous hydroelectric stations on the gorges of the Yangtze and the Yellow River, in a "stair-by-stair" way of development.

Kunlun Mountains in western China

Map of China's Terrain

1.3 Natural Resources

Natural resources are an important component of natural conditions. They include mainly land resources, water resources, climatic resources, biological resources and mineral resources. China has rich natural resources.

Being a vast country, China first of all has rich land resources. The country's farmland covers 951,000 sq. km, about 10% of its total land area, and is distributed mainly in plain areas in northeast China, north China, the middle and lower reaches of the Yangtze, the Sichuan Basin and the Pearl River Delta. Agriculture is highly developed in these areas, which are major producers of wheat,

corn, rice and cash crops.The country has 67,500 sq. km of fresh water lakes -- production bases for fish, shrimps and other aquatic products.

With regard to water resources: China's average total rainfall in a year amounts to 6 trillion cubic meters; the total runoff of its rivers is 2.7 trillion cubic meters; and its total water resources reach 2.8 trillion cubic meters, to rank sixth in the world, after Brazil, Russia, Canada, the United States and Indonesia. Theoretical hydropower resources provided by the country's rivers amount to 676 million kw, of which 378 million kw can be exploited for power generation, ranking first in

A virgin forest in the Greater Hinggan Mountains in northeast China

the world. The distribution of such hydropower resources is uneven: they are concentrated in southwest China.

China has deposits of every one of the 150 minerals found so far in the natural world. The amount of proven deposits in the country has been made clear for 135 of them. Of these, more than 20 rank in the forefront of the world. Ranking first in the world, in proven deposits, are 12 minerals: tungsten, antimony, titanium, vanadium, zinc, rare earth, magnesite, pyrite, fluorite, barite, plaster stone and graphite; ranking second and third are six: tin, mercury, asbestos, talcum, coal and molybdenum; and ranking fourth are five: nickel, lead, iron, manganese and the platinum family. China ranks third in the world in the deposit of 45 important minerals. It is one of a few countries where

White-lipped deer, unique to China, live in high-altitude areas such as the Qinghai-Tibet Plateau.

David's deer have returned to China after being extinct in its native land for decades.

mineral deposits are rich and varieties are fairly complete.

China has fairly rich plant and animal resources. It is home to 32,800 higher plant varieties and 104,000 animal varieties. Among them are some that are quite rare, including the giant panda, the golden monkey, the Yangtze alligator, white-flag dolphin, the metasequoia and the dove tree -- all are "living fossils" that are found nowhere else. To protect wildlife and its ecological environment, China has built a fairly big number of nature reserves, including fourteen that are part of the United Nations' "Man and Biosphere" nature reserve system.

White-crowned cranes are found in swamp areas in northeast China.

China also has vast tidal beach land and rich marine resources. Of its 280,000 sq. km of off-coast sea areas, 260,000 sq. km are fit for aquiculture. Its tidal beach land covers 20,800 sq. km. The country's salt pans produce 17 million tons of salt a year, one third of the world's total. This output ranks China as the biggest salt producer in the world. Marine fish varieties number more than

2,600, including more than 50 that are of high economic value. The country's marine fishing industry and aquiculture are of considerable size. In the country's territorial waters have been found more than 20 minerals, including petroleum, natural gas, iron, copper, phosphorite and glauconite. Extraction has begun for some of them. Petroleum, for example, is being produced from the Beibu Gulf of the South China Sea and from the Bohai Sea off north China. China's marine energy resources are estimated to reach 540 million kw. Development on a small scale has also begun. For example, tidal waves have been used to generate power.

In absolute terms, China indeed abounds in natu-

Cathay silver firs in Sichuan's Jinfoshan Nature Reserve, a precious tree species unique to China

Hulun Buir Grassland in Inner Mongolia

ral resources of various kinds. But, owing to its huge population, its per-capita natural resources, such as land, water and mineral resources, are not rich. Besides, the geographical distribution of its natural resources is not even. Take coal for example: of more than 760 billion tons of total coal deposits, more than 70% are concentrated in Shanxi, Shaanxi and Inner Mongolia, whereas only 1.4% is found in nine provinces in southern China. Of proven recoverable oil deposits, most are found in northeast China, northwest China and coastal areas of north China. 70% of natural gas deposits is concentrated in Sichuan and Shaanxi. The geographical distribution of water is also extremely uneven: in southern China -- areas south of the Huaihe river and the Qinling range, while farmland accounts for only 36.3% of the national total, water resources make up 82.3% of the national

The white-flag dolphin, unique to China, is one of four fresh-water whale varieties in the world. It has a body length of about 2.5 meters.

total; whereas, in northern China, farmland accounts for 63.7% of the national total, water resources make up only 17.7% of the national total; in northwest China, water is even more scarce: while it has one third of the national land area, its water resources account for only 5% of the national total. The distribution of hydropower is also uneven: 70% of the national total is concentrated in southwest China. The Chinese government has been taking measures to deal with the problem. Researches on the issue have been strengthened and overall planning conducted. Concrete measures include the construction of railways to transport more coal from the north to the south and the building of a giant water diversion project to channel water from the Yangtze to the Yellow River to quench thirst in north China and northwest China.

Producing petroleum in the South China Sea

1.4 Population and Ethnic Groups

China has the biggest population in the world. By mid-February 1995, its population had reached 1.2 billion; it further swelled to 1.236 billion by the end of 1997, about 22% of the world's total.

China has a fairly high population density. According to the fourth national census conducted on July 1, 1990, national average population density stood at 118 persons per sq. km. But population density differed sharply in different regions: it stood at 360 persons per sq. km in coastal areas in east China, 197 persons per sq. km in central regions, and only 13 persons per sq. km in western regions. Of the country's 1.2 billion people, about one quarter live in cities and the rest, in rural areas.

China's population has grown fairly rapidly. According to data, the country's population was 540 million in 1949 and grew to 800 million in

1969. Thanks to the government's family planning policy implemented since the beginning of the 1970s, the birth rate went down from 3.411% in 1969 to 1.657% in 1997; and the natural growth rate of the population from 2.608% in 1969 to 1.006% in 1997. Calculated at the natural growth rate in 1970, up to 1997 in the more than 20 years when the family planning policy was implemented, around 300 million fewer people have been added to the country's population.

China is a unified country with 56 nationalities. The Han people account for 92% of the national population, while the other 55 nationalities make up about 8%. They are referred to as ethnic minority people since they have a relatively small population.

Of the 55 ethnic minority groups, those with a population of more than, or close to, 5 million each

The Huis, an ethnic minority people, are concentrated in Ningxia, northwest China. They believe in Islam.

are Zhuang, Manchu, Hui, Yi, Miao, Uygur, Tujia, Tibetan and Mongolian. With a population of more than 15 million, the Zhuang is the biggest ethnic minority group. Ethnic minority groups with a population of less than 100,000 each are Moinba, Oroqen, Drung, Tatar, Hezhen, Gaoshan and Lhoba.

The Han people are distributed most widely: they are found almost everywhere in the country. They are concentrated, however, in northeast China and encatchment areas of the Yellow River, the Yangtze and the Pearl River. The 55 ethnic minority groups, despite having a relatively small combined population, are widely scattered. They are mainly distributed in Inner Mongolia, Xinjiang, Tibet, Guangxi, Ningxia, Heilongjiang, Jilin, Liaoning, Gansu, Qinghai, Sichuan, Yunnan, Guizhou, Hunan and Hubei. Yunnan, home to more than 20 ethnic minority groups, is the Chinese province with the greatest number of nationalities.

Each nationality in China is a member of the great family of the Chinese nation. State policies on nationalities stipulate that all nationalities are equal; that the state shall guarantee all legitimate rights and interests of each nationality, prohibit discrimination and oppression of any nationality, prohibit acts that disrupt unity among the nationalities, and be opposed to big-nationality chauvinism and local-nationality chauvinism; and that each nationality has the freedom to use and develop its

The Zhuangs are the most populous ethnic minority people in China. They are concentrated in Guangxi and most of them are engaged in farming.

Administrative Map of China

own language and script and the freedom to maintain or reform its own customs. The Chinese government has institutionalized a system of autonomy for ethnic minority people. That is to say, under the leadership of the central government, autonomous organs of power are established in areas where ethnic minority people are concentrated; and these organs exercise the power of autonomy, allowing ethnic minority people to run their own local affairs as masters of their own destiny. At present, there are in the country five provincial-level autonomous regions: Guangxi Zhuang Autonomous Region, Inner Mongolia Autonomous Region, Xinjiang Uygur Autonomous Region, Ningxia Hui Autono-

mous Region and Tibet Autonomous Region. There are also many autonomous localities at prefectural, county and township levels.

China has four administrative levels: province (region), county (banner) and township (town), plus prefecture(league) which is above the county and below the province. The first three are basic administrative levels. The names of China's administrative divisions are as follows:

The first level: province, autonomous region and centrally-administered municipality;

The second level: prefecture, league, autonomous prefecture and prefectural-level municipality;

The third level: county, autonomous county, banner, autonomous banner, county-level municipality;

The fourth level: township, minority nationality township, town.

According to China's current administrative division, there are a total of 33 administrative entities at the first level. They are: 23 provinces, five autonomous regions, four centrally-administered municipalities and one special administrative region. Townships and towns are grassroots administrative entities.

China's Provinces, Autonomous Regions, Centrally-Administered Municipalities and Special Administrative Region

Name	Location of government	Area (in sq. km)	Name	Location of government	Area (in sq. km)
Beijing Municipality	Beijing	16,800	Hunan Province	Changsha	210,000
Tianjin Municipality	Tianjin	11,300	Guangdong Province	Guangzhou	186,000
Hebei Province	Shijiazhuang	190,000	Guangxi Zhuang Autonomous Region	Nanning	236,300
Shanxi Province	Taiyuan	156,000	Hainan Province	Haikou	34,000
Inner Mongolia Autonomous Region	Hohhot	1,183,000	Chongqing Municipality	Chongqing	82,000
Liaoning Province	Shenyang	145,700	Sichuan Province	Chengdu	488,000
Jilin Province	Changchun	187,000	Guizhou Province	Guiyang	170,000
Heilongjiang Province	Harbin	469,000	Yunnan Province	Kunming	394,000
Shanghai Municipality	Shanghai	6,200	Tibet Autonomous Region	Lhasa	1,220,000
Jiangsu Province	Nanjing	102,600	Shaanxi Province	Xi'an	205,000
Zhejiang Province	Hangzhou	101,800	Gansu Province	Lanzhou	450,000
Anhui Province	Hefei	139,000	Qinghai Province	Xining	720,000
Fujian Province	Fuzhou	120,000	Ningxia Hui Autonomous Region	Yinchuan	66,400
Jiangxi Province	Nanchang	166,600	Xinjiang Uygur Autonomous Region	Urumqi	1,600,000
Shandong Province	Jinan	153,000	Hong Kong Special Administrative Region	Hong Kong	1,092
Henan Province	Zhengzhou	167,000	Taiwan	Taipei	36,000
Hubei Province	Wuhan	187,400			

1.5 Economic Development

China has a long history of economic development. In close to 2,000 years from the third century B.C. to the 18th century, China was in the forefront of the world in economic, cultural and scientific and technological development. A convincing demonstration of this was ancient China's four great inventions -- the compass, gunpowder, papermaking and printing. In the several hundred years that followed, however, China's social and economic development was extremely slow owing to the fetters of its feudal system and repeated invasions by foreign powers. By the 1940s, China produced annually, only 160,000 tons of steel, 120,000 tons of petroleum, 30 million tons of coal and 1.9 billion meters of cotton cloth, among the least in the world in per-capita terms. Railways open to traffic at the time had a length of only 22,000 km, also among the least in big countries. Even agriculture, touted as the country's economic base, did poorly: in 1949 the country produced only 110 million tons of grain and 450,000 tons of cotton; other crops also suffered from low yields.

After the founding of the People's Republic of China in 1949, the government launched massive economic construction programs centering on the development of a modern industry. This brought rapid economic changes in the country. In the first decade after the founding of New China, viz., in the 1950s, while restoring industrial production capacities damaged in the war, the state concentrated financial and material resources in building big iron and steel bases in Anshan and Bengxi in northeast China, which is rich in needed natural resources and had a fairly strong industrial foundation. At the same time, a number of big factories of key significance were constructed in the Beijing-Tianjin-Tangshan area and in Lanzhou, Wuhan, Xi'an and other places, laying a solid foundation for the country's economic development in years to come.

From the beginning of the 1960s, the state began shifting the focus of capital construction westward, into Sichuan, Qinghai, Ningxia and Guizhou. Built during this period were two big iron and steel complexes, in Sichuan's Panzhihua and Gansu's Jiuquan respectively, and two big coal mines, in Sichuan's Baoding and Guizhou's Liupanshui respectively. At the same time, industries compris-

China's steel industry has laid a foundation for national economic development. Picture shows Daye Steel Works, Hubei Province.

Launching a communications
satellite with a home-made
Long March carrier rocket

ing big enterprises were built in Gansu, Sichuan,
Shaanxi, Hunan and Hubei; the country's second
automotive base was constructed in northwestern
Hubei Province. Massive capital construction during
the period resulted in a number of industrial
belts in the central and western parts of the country:
the Chengdu-Chongqing Industrial Belt, the
Sichuan-Guizhou Industrial Belt centering on
Panzhihua and Liupanshui, the Central Guizhou
Industrial Belt centering on Guiyang, the provincial
capital of Guizhou, the Central Shaanxi Industrial
Belt centering on Xi'an, and the Yellow
River Middle and Upper Reaches Industrial Belt
centering on Lanzhou, the provincial capital of
Gansu. Also constructed during the period were
new industrial bases in western Hubei, western
Henan and western Hunan. The vastly-strength-

ened industries in interior regions have made the distribution of the country's industries more balanced. During the period, the country developed the Daqing Oilfield in Heilongjiang Province in the northeast, making China self-sufficient in petroleum. The oilfield played an important role in the country's economic development.

From the late 1970s, along with the implementation of reform and opening-up policies, many coastal cities were opened to foreign investment and the country's focus of economic development once again began being shifted eastward. Guangdong and Fujian provinces in southeast China, relying on their proximity to Hong Kong and Macao and taking advantage of their being the homeland of many overseas Chinese with great convenience for making contacts with the outside world, lost no time in developing an export-oriented economy. This has enabled them to become the fastest-developing areas in the country economically.

In the early 1990s, the Chinese government decided to establish an economic development zone in Pudong, a Singapore-sized piece of land wedged between Shanghai proper and the East China Sea. This was intended to speed up economic development in Shanghai and let an economically vibrant Shanghai bring about an all-round economic development along the coast and in the Yangtze Valley. Stimulated by massive development of the Pudong Economic Zone, Shanghai indeed has de-

In China with a huge population and limited arable land, agriculture is the foundation of all foundations.

veloped at a high speed economically in recent years.

Up to now, China has had a fairly complete industrial system of a considerable size; and the system as a whole has reached a fairly high level technologically, too. In 1997, China produced 1.39 billion tons of raw coal, 107 million tons of steel (including 97 million tons of steel products), 160 million tons of petroleum and 510 million tons of cement; power generation reached 1,132 billion kwh. China ranked first in the world in the production of raw coal and cement. Today, the country also ranks in the world's forefront in the production of consumer electronics and home appliances such as television sets and refrigerators.

Agricultural production was restored and has had fairly rapid development too. In the 26 years from 1952 to 1978, the agricultural sector provided as much as 800 billion yuan as investment funds for the country's industrialization; agriculture itself underwent fairly rapid development, as did the construction of farmland and irrigation facilities as well as farm mechanization. Beginning from 1978, the government began implementing a series of new rural policies aimed at speeding up agricultural development, the most important being the adoption of the household responsibility contract system. Under the system, land, which continues to be owned collectively as a precondition, is contracted out to individual rural households. This system has fired farmers with great

Ships in the East China Sea

Map of China's Railway System

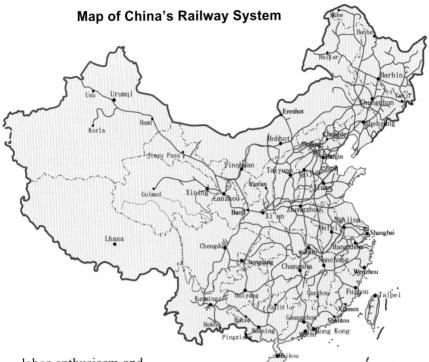

labor enthusiasm and quickly brought about heartening changes to rural China. The family-based farming system has not only promoted an overall development of crop cultivation but also boosted the development of family-based animal husbandry and aquiculture; it has also led to the emergence and development of township industries. In the meantime, the family-based farming system has liberated a considerable part of the rural surplus labor. Large numbers of farmers have since migrated into cities as an abundant source of labor for urban construction projects.

With their own efforts, the Chinese people, who

account for 22% of the world's total population, have been able to feed themselves with only 7% of the world's total farmland. In 1997, China produced 492 million tons of grain, 4.3 million tons of cotton, 21.5 million tons of oil-bearing seeds, 53.54 million tons of meat and 35.61 million tons of aquatic products. These are among the world's biggest national outputs. Within the agricultural sector, grain production has increased steadily, cash crops developed at a rapid pace, and forestry, animal husbandry and fisheries grown even more rapidly, ensuring that they meet growing demand from the national economy as well as from people living a far better life than before.

At present, China's national economy has reached a considerable size. In 1997, its gross domestic product (GDP) amounted to 7.4772 trillion yuan (US$903 billion), ranking China among the

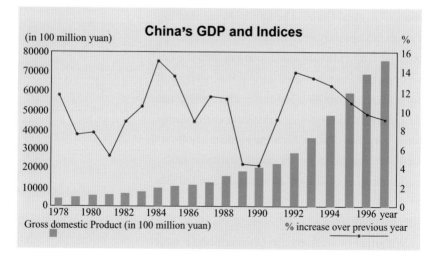

China's GDP and Indices

(in 100 million yuan)

Gross domestic Product (in 100 million yuan)

% increase over previous year

top ten countries in the world in economic strength. China's per-capita GDP, however, is still relatively small. China is still a low-income developing country.

China has achieved remarkable progress in transportation and telecom too. It has built a comprehensive transportation system comprising railways, highways, waterways, civil aviation and pipelines. It has also built national telecom and postal networks. In 1997, railways open to traffic had a total length of 66,000 km, inland waterways open to navigation 110,000 km, highways open to traffic 1.214 million km, and civil aviation routes 1.425 million km. Major ports along the coast now have more than 1,300 berths.

Transportation equipment and equipment used by the telecom and postal sectors have been upgraded. The proportion of double-track railways and that of electrified ones have both gone up; advanced technologies have been used extensively. The proportion of high-grade highways has increased. A number of special berths for coal, mineral ores and containers have been built along the coast; further progress has been made in loading and unloading mechanization at ports; and a far greater number of big bulk, container and ro-ro ships are in use. China's aircraft fleet for civil aviation has kept expanding, with such big aircraft as Boeing 747s and Boeing 757s having become the mainstay of the fleet. In the country's telcom networks, program-controlled switching, transmission

China has invested heavily in infrastructure development in recent years. Picture shows the Beijing-Tianjin-Tanggu Expressway.

In densely-populated east China, land supports an excessive population load.

by way of optical fiber cables, satellites and microwaves, and mobile telephony have been extensively used. The number of telephone lines nationwide has reached 110 million, and program-controlled switching is used for all telephone networks in Chinese cities above the county level. China's telephone network has become the second biggest in the world.

Despite such impressive progresses, China's economic development focus continues to be the expansion and improvement of infrastructure such as transport and telecom. In the next period, the country will build a number of new trunk railways, upgrade the existing trunk railways, speed up railway electrification and continue to increase the proportion of double-track lines; increase the proportion of expressways in the country's road network; devote major efforts to developing water and air transport; and increase the level of automation in its postal and telecom sectors.

Along with rapid economic development, the proportion of urban population has kept increasing. The last two decades have seen a continuous improvement of public facilities in many big and medium-sized cities and the emergence of numerous new cities. At present, the number of cities in China exceeds 600, compared with 193 in 1978 and 58 in 1949. Among the newly-emerging cities, some have owed their birth to economic development, others are open coastal cities and still others are cultural cities with a long history.

Chapter II
China's Geography: A Regional Survey

According to spatial differences in its natural conditions, China can be divided into three vast regions: the East Monsoon Region, the Northwest Interior Region and the Qinghai-Tibet Plateau Region. The three regions can further be divided into seven geographical areas according to their geographical features: Northeast China, North China, the Middle and Lower reaches of the Yangtze, South China, Southwest China, Northwest China and the Qinghai-Tibet Plateau. These areas have different natural and cultural features.

The rising sun as viewed from the top of Mount Taishan

2.1
The East
Monsoon
Region

The Chinese mainland is subject to strong influence from the Asian East Monsoon, and this is particularly true of east China. The East Monsoon Region mentioned in this book covers the provinces of Heilongjiang, Jilin, Liaoning, Hebei, Shandong, Shanxi, Henan, Shaanxi, Jiangsu, Anhui, Jiangxi, Hunan, Hubei, Fujian, Taiwan, Guangdong, Hainan, Sichuan, Yunnan and Guizhou, the Guangxi Zhuang Autonomous Region, the four centrally-administered municipalities of Beijing, Shanghai, Tianjin and Chongqing, and the Hong Kong Special Administrative Region. The East Monsoon Region has good natural conditions, and is densely populated and economically developed. It is a region that has had rapid economic development since the implementation of the policies of reform and opening to the outside world.

Northeast China

Northeast China comprises Heilongjiang, Jilin and Liaoning provinces administratively. It borders Russia in the north and Korea in the east. Its domestic neighbors are Inner Mongolia in the west and Hebei in the south.

Late but Rapid Development

In the early history of China, northeast China was inhabited by ethnic minority groups. The area's development was relatively late in comparison with the country's hinterland. During the Ming Dynasty (1368-1644), to guard against invasions from ethnic minority groups, the Ming government strengthened defense along the Great Wall running from the Shanhaiguan Pass on the Bohai Sea coast to Jiayu Pass in the northwest and further restricted the settlement and reclamation of land in northeast China by people from central China. It was not until the 18th century that large numbers of people from the country's heartland, with encouragement from the Qing government, emigrated to northeast China. Even then, the northern part of northeast China was still sparsely populated with large tracts of waste land waiting to be reclaimed.

Early this century, development of northeast China entered its peak period. Large numbers of immigrants poured into the region as railways were constructed and forestry, industrial production and mining were developed there. In the 1950s, the state focused on the development of plains in the northern part of the region, establishing a number of large, mechanized farms.

Compared with provinces in the country's heartland, Liaoning has a high population density, Jilin a medium density and Heilongjiang a low density. Of the 100 million people in northeast China, Han Chinese account for more than 90%. Other nationalities in the region are Manchu, Mongolian, Korean, Daur, Oroqen and Hui.

People's customs in northeast China are closely related with local natural conditions. Living in vast, sparsely populated areas with fertile land, local residents are straightforward and of a sanguine dis-

Rime — ice deposited by freezing of supercooled fog — is a common natural sight in winter in northeast China.

position. Owing to freezing cold in winter, traditional residential houses are generally built low with thick walls for better insulation; most residents sleep on the heated bed called *kang*, like to drink fiery alcoholic liquor and eat fat pork. Customs kept by people in the interior areas of the country are also found in northeast China since all immigrants there had come from the rest of China.

Northeast China is where a domestic modern industry developed at a fairly early date. In such cities as Shenyang, Changchun and Harbin, workers constitute a fairly big proportion of the local populations. With influence from a modern industry, residents are fairly well educated. Particularly after the 1950s, big newly-built industrial enterprises and mining operations employed large num-

Riding horse-drawn sledges in northeast China

bers of local residents, turning them into a generation of educated, skilled industrial workers.

Rich in Natural Resources

Northeast China has superior natural conditions. It is encircled by the Greater Hinggan mountain range in the west, the Heilongjiang River and the Lesser Hinggan mountain range in the north and the Yalu River and the Changbai mountain range in the east. At the center is a vast fertile plain -- the Northeast China Plain. The largest in China, the Northeast China Plain comprises three parts: the Liaohe Plain in the south, the Songnen Plain in the north (named after Songhuajiang and Nenjiang rivers flowing past the plain), and the Sanjiang Plain in the northeast (Sanjiang means "three rivers" in Chinese, which refer to Heilongjiang, Songhuajiang and Wusuli rivers). On the Northeast China Plain, winter is long and cold and the annual frost-free period is short, but a short, warm summer provides ample heat for one crop a year. And the plain land is extremely fertile. As a result, the Northeast China Plain has a well-developed agriculture and has become China's important commodity grain production base.

Daur people in northeast China keep reindeer, whose pilose antlers are a precious medicine.

Grain crops in northeast China are mainly corn, sorghum, soy bean, rice and spring wheat. Corn takes up the biggest proportion of farmland and yield is also the highest. The region has a long history of sorghum cultivation with production areas widely scattered. Soy bean is the best-known farm product of the Northeast China Plain. Locally produced soy beans are of superior quality. Heilongjiang Province is the country's biggest producer of soy beans. Spring wheat is concentrated in Heilongjiang Province's Land Reclamation Area built in the last four decades, where mechanization is high and commodity grain production has exceeded 30%. Besides, northeast China is a major producer of sugar beet and flax.

Large tracts of forests cover mountain ranges on the fringes of northeast China. The region, therefore, ranks first in China in terms of forest coverage, the amount of standing timber and timber output. The Greater Hinggan Range is covered mainly by larch forests, and the Changbai Range by mixed forests of Chinese pines and deciduous broad-leaved trees. Korean pines that grow on the Lesser Hinggan Range are a fine-quality building material. Years of felling have seriously reduced the coverage of virgin forests in northeast China. At present, only in the northern section of the Greater Hinggan Range can large tracts of virgin forest still be found.

Forests in northeast China are home to many rare and precious animals. The mountainous areas of the region have long been known as the source of "Three Treasures of Northeast China:" ginseng, marten pelt and pilose antler. After years of trial and error, people have succeeded in cultivating ginseng on large tracts of land in the mountains, and in breeding and raising deer and martens. The

The Northeast China Plain is one of China's important granaries.

Northeast China provides half of all timber in China.

Changbai Range is the habitat of the world's biggest tiger -- the Manchurian Tiger. Killing by men has reduced the tiger on the verge of extinction. To protect precious animals and plants and to facilitate scientific research, the state has established nature reserves in the Changbai and Lesser Hinggan mountain ranges. The Changbai Mountain Nature Reserve is the largest in area and has joined the United Nations' "Man and Biosphere" network of nature reserves.

The Largest Heavy Industrial Base

Northeast China, especially a vast area around Shenyang in central-south Liaoning Province, has rich mineral deposits of adequate varieties for the development of a heavy industry there. Deposits include iron, coal and iron-making auxiliary materials. And, in the amount of deposit, these minerals are fairly proportionate. Iron ores are produced mainly in Anshan, Benxi and Liaoyang, and coal in Fushun and Benxi. The two resources are not located far from each other. In fact, Benxi produces both iron ore and coal.

As early as the beginning of this century, the central-south region of Liaoning had developed a steel industry of a considerable size comprising iron ore mining, iron smelting and steel making. The steel industry also gave rise to a booming machine-building industry. In the 1950s following the founding of New China, the state invested heavily in this heavy industrial base, expanding and renovating the iron and steel works in Anshan and Benxi and building a number of big machine-building plants devoted mainly to the manufacturing of heavy machinery. This turned central-south Liaoning into China's largest heavy industrial base. Up to now, heavy industry still has a fairly big proportion in northeast China's economy. Liaoning has the highest proportion of heavy industry among the country's provinces, autonomous regions and

A scene in Daqing Oilfield in Heilongjiang Province

centrally-administered municipalities.

Northeast China's heavy industry comprises mainly metallurgy and the manufacturing of heavy machine tools and power generating equipment. The region's coal, petroleum, petrochemicals and automotive industries also have an important place in the country. The Anshan-Benxi Iron and Steel Base, comprising the Anshan Iron and Steel Corporation and the Benxi Iron and Steel (Group) Co., Ltd., supply steel products and pig iron to customers around the country.

A car assembly workshop in the First Automotive Works in Changchun, Jilin Province

The Northeast China Plain has rich deposits of petroleum and natural gas. In the late 1950s, petroleum was discovered in Heilongjiang Province's Songnen Plain. Soon after, oil production reached a considerable level and the area was named Daqing Oilfield. Beginning from 1963, China became self-sufficient in petroleum, and the main source of petroleum was Daqing. Today, Daqing is still China's biggest oilfield and has maintained an annual crude output of more than 50 million tons for many years. Following Daqing, two other oilfields -- Liaohe and Jilin -- were developed in northeast China. The region thus produces more than half of the national total output of petroleum.

The First Automotive Works in Changchun (now the First Automotive Group Co.) was the first of its kind in China manufacturing mainly medium-duty trucks. Its improved Jiefang (Liberation) truck, which has stable quality and is fuel efficient, is a leading truck model in China. Since the mid-

1980s, the First Automotive Group Co. has been shifting its focus to making light vehicles and cars.

Shenyang and Dalian -- Important Cities in Northeast China

Shenyang, the provincial capital of Liaoning, is the largest industrial city in northeast China. It is also the region's transportation hub and economic center. It has a population of five million today. In history, Shenyang was the secondary capital city of China's last monarchy -- the Qing Dynasty (1644-1911). The palatial complex at the center of the city has been well preserved. Other well-known places of historical interest in Shenyang include the East Mausoleum and the North Mausoleum where are buried the two founders of the Qing Dynasty -- Nu'er Hachi and Huang Taiji.

Shenyang is a close neighbor of Anshan and Benxi, both steel producers. Nor is it far from Fushun, a coal producer. To the south of Shenyang lies the port city of Dalian, and the two cities are linked by a railway and an expressway. Rich in mineral resources and being a transportation hub, Shenyang has all the conditions to develop itself into a heavy industrial base. The city at present is the biggest machine tools production center in China. It is also a major producer of big blower fans, big pumps and big transformers.

Dalian is located at the southern tip of the Liaodong Peninsula and is the southern starting point of the Shenyang-Dalian Railway and the

A steel rolling workshop of Anshan Iron & Steel orporation in Liaoning Province

Dalian—a port city

Shenyang-Dalian Expressway. It is the coastal gateway for northeast China. Dalian is a deep-water port with a broad harbor area free of ice all the year round. A crude oil terminal has been built at the Nianyuwan Bay to the north of Dalian's existing dock area and is linked with Daqing Oilfield by a pipeline. Today, the port of Dalian has close to 30 berths able to accommodate 10,000-dwt ships. Berths with the greatest water depths can receive 50,000-100,000-dwt ships. Dalian is the second largest multiple-function sea port in China after Shanghai and ranks third in cargo handling capacity after Shanghai and Qinhuangdao.

North China

North China comprises the five provinces of Hebei, Shandong, Henan, Shanxi and Shaanxi and the two centrally-administered municipalities of Beijing and Tianjin. It is located in the middle and lower reaches of the Yellow River. Its western part

Hops are a necessary ingredient of beer. Picture shows ethnic Koreans in northeast China harvesting hops.

is the Loess Plateau, and its eastern part is the North China Plain, with the Yellow River cutting across the whole area. The Yellow River Culture -- the representative of Chinese civilization -- originated here.

Long History, Ancient Cultural Traditions

North China is an important birthplace of the Chinese nation. Unearthed cultural relics show that the Peking Man found at Beijing's Zhoukoudian and the Lantian Man found in Shaanxi were ancestors of the Chinese nation who lived about 500,000-600,000 years ago and 800,000 years ago respectively. In the New Stone Age about 5,000-6,000 years ago, ancient human beings made North China their home. Unearthed articles show that groups of primitive people had by then developed a primitive agriculture and animal husbandry. The Banpo Ruins near Xi'an, Shaanxi Province, has all the characteristics of a New Stone Age culture. The mausoleum of Emperor Huang Di, the Chinese nation's legendary ancestor, is located on Mount Qiaoshan in Shaanxi's Huangling County, and the three ancient emperors after Huang Di -- Yao, Shun and Yu -- all left their foot prints in the lower reaches of the Fenhe River. The Xia Dynasty (circa 22nd century-17th century B.C.) and the Shang Dynasty (circa 17th century-11th century B.C.), China's earliest states practicing a slave system, conducted their main activities in North China. *Yin Xu*, or the ruins of the Yin Dynasty, at the present-day Xiaotun Village in Anyang, Henan, was the capital city of the Shang Dynasty in its latter period (Shang changed its name into Yin after moving its capital to the city of Yin, present-day Xiaotun Village). By then, China was a full-fledged slave society and had a developed bronze smelting industry. Judged from engravings on unearthed animal bones, Chinese characters had taken initial shape more than 3,000 years ago. Emperor Qin Shihuang, a man of great talent and bold vision, using the Huihe River Plain in present-day Shaanxi Province as his base, unified China under Qin (221-206 B.C.), the dynasty he established. The Han Dynasty (206 B.C.-220 A.D.) and the Tang Dynasty (618-907), the two peaks of China's feudal society, both had their capital in Chang'an (present-day Xi'an). During long periods after

Shanhaiguan Pass, the starting point of the Great Wall in the east. It is the gateway from the North China Plain to northeast China.

Tang, the North China Plain continued to be one of China's most economically developed areas and home to the country's political center. Of China's seven ancient capital cities, North China claims five: Xi'an, Beijing and Henan's Anyang, Luoyang and Kaifeng. These cities are rich in historical sites and relics. Xi'an, today as a well-known tourist city with historical sites as its main attractions, is second only to Beijing. At the mausoleum of Emperor Qin Shihuang near Xi'an, two pits containing a huge army of terra-cotta soldiers and horses have been open to the public after years of excavation. The army of clay soldiers and horses--burial articles for the dead emperor -- is reputed to be the "Eighth Wonder of the World."

China's traditional culture has a long history. It has two sources: Confucianism represented by Confucius and Taoism represented by Laozi.

Confucius (551-479 B.C.) was a great thinker, statesman, educationist and the founder of Confucianism. He had reportedly 3,000 disciples, of whom more than 70 were well known in history. Confucian teachings are mainly contained in a number of Confucian classics compiled by the first few generations of Confucius' disciples, chiefly *Lun Yu* (Analects), *Zhong Yong* (the Confucian Doctrine of the Mean), *Da Xue* (Great Learning) and *Mengzi* (the Book of Mencius). Confucius and his principal successor Mencius carried out their activities mainly in Shandong's Qifu and Zouxian areas, and their Confucian teachings, after being sorted out by scholars and promoted by feudal rulers in different historical periods, have become the mainstream of traditional Chinese thinking and exerted far-reaching influences on the oriental culture as well as Chinese culture. As a result, Confucius has been reputed to be one of the world's ten leading thinkers in ancient times. Laozi, also a thinker active in the Spring and Autumn Period (770-476 B.C.), was the founder of Taoism. Before he quit from an official job, Laozi had served the Zhou Dynasty as a historian in charge of books and records. In his early years, he engaged mainly in academic activities in Luoyang, the capital city of the Zhou Dynasty, and left behind a very important philosophical classic entitled *Dao De Jing*, or Classic of the Virtue of the Tao. Both Confucius and Laozi were sons of North China. Confucianism and Taoism founded and represented by them

With a rich cultural heritage and natural beauty, Mount Taishan is a great tourist attraction.

respectively have influenced Chinese culture for more than 2,000 years and, to a certain extent, continue to have practical significance today.

Qufu, the hometown of Confucius, is full of landmarks related with the ancient sage. The best-known are: the Confucius Temple, the Confucius Clan Cemetery and the Confucius Mansion. In Zouxian County are three Mencius-related landmarks: the Mencius Temple, the Mencius Clan Cemetery and the Mencius Mansion, which are smaller than, but are similar in layout to, the Confucius-related structures. The sites in Qufu and Zouxian, regarded as "the hometowns of Confucius and Mencius and the birthplaces of enlightenment," long received the utmost attention from rulers and scholars of different dynasties. They were repeatedly renovated and now keep a great number of cultural relics of great historical value.

Not far to the north of the hometowns of Confucius and Mencius towers Mount Taishan, worshipped as the first among five most famous mountains in China (the others are Huashan in Shaanxi, Hengshan in Shanxi, Hengshan in Hunan and Songshan in Henan. Of the five, four are located in North China except Mount Hengshan in Hunan). A line in an ancient poem says: "Climbing up Mount Taishan, one finds a diminished world all around." The main peak of Mount Taishan called the Jade Emperor Top rises 1,545 meters above sea level, majestic and imposing. The Dai Temple at the foot of the mountain, one of the biggest ancient buildings in China, keeps quite a few stone tablets bearing famous inscriptions. Flanking the mountain path that leads to the summit are a great number of rock-face inscriptions that have the same value as cultural treasures.

Longmen Caves near Luoyang, Henan Province. Built 1,500 years ago, the caves house more than 100,000 Buddhist statues.

The Loess Plateau, Unique in the World

Topographically, north China comprises mainly the North China Plain and the Loess Plateau.

The Loess Plateau constitutes the western part of north China, and the North China Plain its eastern part. The two are separated by the Taihang Mountain Range and belong respectively to the second and first of China's three altitudinal stairs. Topographically, the Loess Plateau and the North China Plain are interrelated: deposits of the fine yellowish-gray soil of the Loess Plateau are the raw material for the formation of the North China Plain, while big and small rivers including the Yellow River are the "belt conveyer" of this material. It is evident that there would not have been today's

North China Plain without the Loess Plateau.

China's Loess Plateau is unique in the world. It is vast, covering more than 300,000 sq. km; and loess deposit is thick with a maximum thickness of 200 meters at some places. The soil on the plateau is yellowish gray and soft. The plateau's unique landform, which has resulted from erosion by wind and rain, consists of three loess types: the *yuan*, the *liang* and the *mao*. *Yuan* means plain, originally the dominant landform on the Loess Plateau, where farmland is flat and villages are located close to one another. Today, it is difficult to find large *yuan* tracts on the plateau. *Liang* is a narrow strip of land sandwiched by two gullies. A *liang*, after being cut further by forces of nature, becomes numerous *mao*s -- separate flat-topped hills. That is why some people liken the Loess Plateau to "a world molded by a crazy god." There is no consensus as to how the loess has come into being. According to a fairly prevalent theory, the huge amounts of yellowish soil on the Loess Plateau had been blown from central Asian deserts in a distant geological era by strong winds. The formation of the Loess Plateau, according to an estimate by scientists, took hundreds of thousands of years.

Originally, the Loess Plateau was a verdant land with grass growing on elevated plains and small tracts of forests scattered in low-lying areas. Thousands of years of human activities -- grazing, land reclamation and the felling of trees -- destroyed

Cave dwellings on the Loess Plateau

virgin grasslands and forests; erosion by wind and rain left countless numbers of gullies, big and small, on the plateau. Viewed from a flying plane, the irregular gullies look like big and small tree branches engraved on land. It is a unique picture, but the viewer is in no mood to enjoy such a picture.

With a high calcium carbonate content, the loess

Mount Wutaishan in Shanxi Province is one of China's four mountain shrines dedicated to Buddhism.

is hard when dry but becomes instantly soft when wet. It goes wherever rain water flows. This is the root cause why the Loess Plateau suffers from the most serious soil erosion in China.

Large amounts of mud and sand resulting from loess erosion have made the Yellow River, which cuts through the plateau, the most muddy river in the world. The Yellow River carries downstream as much as 1.6 billion tons of sand a year.

There are quite a number of rivers on the Loess Plateau. Besides the Yellow River, there are its tributaries: Weihe, Jinghe, Fenhe, Sushui and Yanhe. Valleys created by these rivers such as the Fenhe Valley and the Weihe Valley have good irrigation conditions and are major producers of wheat and cotton. They are the richest and most populous areas on the Loess Plateau.

The Loess Plateau as viewed from above

Harnessing and Utilization of the Yellow River

The Yellow River is the second longest in China. Originating from the Yaogu Zonglie Basin at the northern foot of the Bayanhar Range in Qinghai Province, the river runs eastward, over a distance of 5,460 km, to the sea, passing through nine provinces and regions: Qinghai, Sichuan, Gansu, Ningxia, Inner Mongolia, Shanxi, Shaanxi, Henan and Shandong. It empties into the Bohai Sea at Kenli County, Shandong. Main tributaries of the river are, from west to east, Huangshui, Taohe, Jinghe, Weihe, Luohe, Fenhe, Yihe and Qinhe. The Yellow River system has an encatchment area of 752,400 sq. km and the Yellow River has an annual runoff of 48 billion cubic meters. The river flows pass vast fertile farmland, lush natural pasturelands and huge deposits of mineral resources. The Yellow River encatchment area and areas along the river's lower reaches have more than 20 million hectares of farmland and a population of 110 million.

Comprehensive efforts at soil erosion control have changed the landscape of the Dingxi area in Gansu Province.

The Yellow River is divided customarily into upper, middle and lower sections. The upper section runs from the river source to Inner Mongolia's Tuoketuo, the middle section from Tuoketuo to Henan's Mengjin, and the lower section from Mengjin to the sea. The upper Yellow River, flowing on the Qinghai-Tibet Plateau, has a stable runoff volume and contains little sand. The middle section, cutting across the Loess Plateau, carries large amounts of silt, which dyes the river yellow,

The Yellow River cuts through the Tengger Desert in the southwestern part of the Inner Mongolia Steppe. Scattered in the area are residual mountains, flat land, sand dunes and lake basins.

hence its name. The Yellow River is unique in the world in that every cubic meter of its water contains as much as 37.6 kg of sand.

As it enters the North China Plain, the Yellow River abruptly slows down its flow, causing the silt it carries to settle down and the riverbed to keep rising. Years of sedimentation have caused the lower section of the Yellow River to become a "hanging" river. According to surveys, the bed of the lower section of the Yellow River rises at a rate of as much as 10 centimeters a year. Once the riverbed is higher than the surrounding ground, the Yellow River's flooding and change of course is inevitable. According to historical records, during the past 2,500 years, the Yellow River burst its banks more than 1,500 times and had 26 major changes of course. That is a rate of two breaches every three years, and their effect was felt as far north as Tianjin and as south as the Huaihe River. In fact, traces of the Yellow River's course changes can be found everywhere in the North China Plain. Every flooding and course change of the Yellow River was a catastrophe for people living along its lower reaches. "Flood waters overflowed the banks and dead human bodies floated everywhere" and "A thousand *li* (one half of a km) of barren land strewn with bodies of the starved," as recorded in historical documents, are a truthful description of disasters caused by the Yellow River. That is why the river is called "China's sorrow."

But the Yellow River is a great river. Its water

has nurtured a people who created one of the world's most ancient cultures -- the Yellow River Culture, which prospered for thousands of years.

Since the founding of New China in 1949, the Yellow River has entered a new historical period. The stability and economic development of the country have provided good conditions for the harnessing of the Yellow River. The Chinese government has invested heavily in consolidating and heightening the river's embankments and delimited a number of low-lying areas along it for flood detention and storage. Along the river's middle section, efforts for water and soil conservation have persisted and produced marked results. On the river's middle and upper sections have been constructed a number of large projects that generate

The Yellow River, Chinese people's "mother river"

electricity and supply water in addition to regulating, blocking and storing flood waters. During the 50 years since the founding of New China, the Yellow River has not breached its banks or changed its course despite the fact that heavy rain swelled its flow to dangerous levels on several occasions, proving that efforts at its harnessing have been effective.

Development of the Yellow River's hydropower has attracted attention at home and abroad. The river's 4,600-km upper and middle sections contain rich hydropower resources. This is especially true of a 1,000-km section from Ningxia's Qingtong Gorge upward to Qinghai's Longyang Gorge: with more than one-third of the Yellow River's total runoff and a drop of more than 1,300 meters in elevation, it contains 13 million kw in hydropower resources, more than half of the Yellow River's total. It is ideal for a stair-by-stair development of the river's hydropower.

Small streams on the Qinghai-Tibet Plateau — the source of the Yellow River.

The Yellow River's hydropower resources are especially concentrated along a 335-km section from Lanzhou to the Longyang Gorge. Two dams, each more than 100 meters high, have been built on this section, one at the Longyang Gorge and the other at the Liujia Gorge. The Longyang Gorge dam has created a reservoir with a water storage capacity of 26.8 billion cubic meters and the Liujia Gorge dam, a reservoir with a capacity of 5.7 billion cubic meters. Built on this section are also Bapan Gorge and Yanguo Gorge hydroelectric stations. Total power generation capacity has reached 3.1 million kw.

With numerous gorges, the upper section of the Yellow River has rich hydropower resources. Picture shows the Liujia Gorge Hydroelectric Station on the section in Gansu Province.

Downstream from Lanzhou, hydroelectric stations have been constructed at Qingtong Gorge, Sanshenggong, Tianqiao and Sanmenxia Gorge. The last, built in 1957 near the city of Sanmenxia in Henan Province, is the first on the Yellow River. The Sanmenxia Gorge Project was intended to control flood waters in the river's middle and upper sections. Designers of the project, however, under-estimated the amount of silt carried by the Yellow River. Serious silting in the reservoir necessitated repeated rework on the project. The reworked Sanmenxia Gorge Project can effectively release silt as well as generate power -- a guarantee for its long-term operation. The success of the project's transformation has provided valuable experience for constructing large water control projects on muddy rivers.

To further harness the Yellow River, a big reservoir with a water storage capacity of 5 billion cubic meters is being built at Xiaolangdi, Henan, just before the river enters the North China Plain. The Xiaolangdi Reservoir will be used in combination with the Sanmenxia Reservoir to enable the Yellow River to withstand especially mighty floods that happen once every 1,000 years rather than smaller floods that happen once every 60 years, as is the case now.

China's Biggest Energy Base

North China is China's biggest energy base. It has rich deposits of coal, petroleum and natural gas. The Loess Plateau abounds in coal. In Shanxi Province, almost every county has coal deposits. Also rich in coal is Shaanxi Province, where deposits are linked with those at Inner Mongolia's Junggar and Dongsheng to become almost a contiguous vast coal field -- one of China's energy bases in the 21st century.

A coal jetty at the port of Qinhuangdao, Hebei Province, used for shipping coal from Shanxi

The Shengli Oilfield in Shandong Province

Shanxi coal was formed mainly in the Paleozoic Era and the early period of the Mesozoic Era 100-200 million years ago. Coal deposits have been found under one-third of the total area of the province, or 60,000 sq. km. They are concentrated in six coal fields: Datong, Ningwu, Xishan, Huoxian, Qinshui and Hedong, where combined proven coal deposits exceed 200 billion tons, one-third of the national total. Coal from these areas is of good quality and of a whole range of varieties. Shanxi coal has a low ash, sulfur and phosphorus content and a high calorific capacity. Furthermore, coal deposits in Shanxi are easy to mine thanks to simple geological structures, and stable and shallow coal seams. After years of construction, Shanxi has become China's biggest coal supply base with an annual output of more than 200 million tons, about one-fifth of the national total. Datong in northern Shanxi is the country's biggest coal mine and one of a few biggest in the world. Datong produces mainly power-generating coal known at home and abroad for its superior quality. The Yangquan Coal Mine is the country's biggest producer of anthracite. Shanxi coal is exported as well as supplied to other parts of the country.

Shaanxi coal is produced mainly from Tongchuan. The last two decades have seen the discovery of larger coal and natural gas fields in northern Shaanxi -- the Shenfu (Shenmu-Fugu) Coal Field and the Yanan Natural Gas Field. The amount of coal reserves at Shenfu exceeds the total previously found in all of Shaanxi. These together with coal deposits lying close by in the neighboring Inner Mongolia make a world-class super large coal field. The Shenfu Coal Field now under development is expected to play a key role in China's energy supplies in the 21st century.

The Antaibao open-cast coal mine in Pingshuo, Shanxi Province

To transport coal out of Shanxi, concentrated efforts have been made to build railways and highways that link the province with the rest of the country. The last three decades have seen the building of Beijing-Yuanping, Taiyuan-Jiaozuo and Datong-Qinhuangdao railways, in addition to the existing Beijing-Baotou and Taiyuan-Shijiazhuang railways. The new Datong-Qinhuangdao Railway, electrified and with heavy rails, has a carrying capacity of 100 million tons a year. A modern coal-handling dock has been built at the port of Qinhuangdao, allowing large amounts of Shanxi coal to be shipped to the international market as well as to the country's coastal provinces and cities. In the meantime, a number of pit-head power plants have been built at coal mines, their power transmitted to cities on the North China Plain via high-voltage transmission lines.

North China is also rich in petroleum resources. It is home to a number of big oilfields -- Shengli in the Yellow River delta, Dongpu at a Shandong-Hebei border area and Renqiu in central Hebei.

The Middle and Lower Reaches of the Yangtze

This region covers the six provinces of Jiangsu, Zhejiang, Anhui, Jiangxi, Hunan and Hubei, and Shanghai municipality. It is different from north China in terms of natural conditions, land utilization and people's lifestyle.

A Region of Rivers and Lakes

A distinct east-west geographical demarcation

line cuts through the eastern half of China. It is called the Qinling Range-Huaihe River Line. In areas south of this line, annual precipitation exceeds 800 mm, temperatures are slightly higher than in the north of the country, and rivers are not frozen in winter. If you take a train from Beijing to Shanghai, you will find that, after the train goes past the Huaihe River, an increasing number of paddy-fields come into view, as do rivers and lakes. You have come to a land made distinct from the rest of the country by an abundance of water. The region is home to China's five largest fresh water lakes: Poyang, Dongting, Taihu, Hongze and Chaohu.

Surrounding each lake is usually a fertile, densely-populated plain less than 50 meters above sea level. With good irrigation facilities and a very high rate of land utilization, the plains are important "granaries" in southern China. The Yangtze River Delta and the Taihu Lake Plain are most characteristic of water-abundant southern China. Here, the flat land is crisscrossed by rivers and

Hilly areas south of the Yangtze are a major producer of rice, tea and citrus fruit

dotted with lakes; and here, paddy-fields, fish ponds, mulberry gardens, bamboo groves and cottages make an enchanting picture of "a land of fish and rice."

People living in this region cannot do without water. The locals grow rice in the paddy-fields, plant lotus in lakes and engage in fish-and-shrimp farming. Crisscrossing rivers are important routes of transportation for the locals.

"Land of fish and rice" south of the Yangtze River

Abundant water resources have beautified city environment in southern China. "There is paradise up above and there are Suzhou and Hangzhou down on earth" has been a popular saying since ancient times. That is to say, Suzhou in Jiangsu Province and Hangzhou in Zhejiang Province are as beautiful as paradise in popular perceptions. In areas south of the Yangtze, other cities made beautiful by water include Yangzhou in Jiangsu and Shaoxing in Zhejiang.

Suzhou has a history of 2,500 years, dating back to the State of Wu during the Warring States Period (770-476 B.C.). The city has a unique layout: streets and rivers go in parallel, with houses opening onto the streets and their back doors leading to the rivers. Residents can fetch water through the back doors. Vegetables and foodstuffs are transported to the doors of people's residences through these rivers. Hundreds of bridges of different styles span the rivers to connect the entire city. That is why Suzhou is often called "Venice in the Orient." Gardens in Suzhou are a treasure in traditional Chinese architecture. Designers create scenery by imitating nature: first a pond is dug, with the excavated earth piled up to make a mound or a hill; pavilions and buildings are then constructed and various trees and flowers planted. The idea is to allow people "to enjoy the beauty of nature without going out of town."

The beauty of Hangzhou lies in West Lake. A poem singing its praise by Su Dongpo (1037-1101), a highly-accomplished man of letters living in the Song Dynasty, reads: "It looks good on a clear day when water plays with light; it makes people marvel, too, on a rainy day when distant hills are shrouded in mist. Like Lady Xi Shi (an ancient beauty), the West Lake is beautiful on all occasions." Both Suzhou and Hangzhou are the most famous tourist cities in China.

An ancient Chinese saying goes: "The benevolent take delight in living near mountains and the wise, near waters." The richly-endowed land of rivers and lakes south of the Yangtze has been home to many talented people, including Lu Xun, Mao Dun, Yu Dafu and Ye Shengtao, all well-known men of letters in China's modern history.

Taihu Lake in Jiangsu Province

Land with a Rich Variety of Produce

The middle and lower reaches of the Yangtze are one of China's bread baskets. The Jianghan Plain in Hubei, the Dongting Lake Plain, the Poyang Lake Plain, the Taihu Lake Plain and the Yangtze River Delta have always been China's

The ancient city of Suzhou, Jiangsu Province

most important "land of fish and rice." Here, the land is fertile, rainfall is plentiful and irrigation facilities are good. Two crops are grown a year -- usually rape or spring wheat followed by rice; and in some areas, even two crops of rice are cultivated a year. Per-unit-area yield of crops here is far higher than in northeast China and north China. Wheat, rape and cotton are grown here in addition to rice. The region is the biggest producer of rice and rapeseed in the country.

Fish farming is well developed in the region which, as a result, is also China's biggest producer of fresh water fish. Four major fish species are raised here: the common carp, the black carp, the bighead and the silver carp. Special fish species in this region include the blunt-snout bream, the whitebait and the Chinese perch. River crabs and shrimps are common in the region. Cultivated aquatic plants include lotus, water caltrop, arrowhead and water chestnut.

The Taihu Lake Plain is an important silk production base with a long history. Local people have rich experience in cultivating mulberry trees and raising silkworms. The government has established here a sericulture research institute, which promotes the use of scientific methods to raise silkworms and popularizes fine silkworm species. Silkworm raising in this area is highly productive and the silk cocoons produced here are of high quality. Cities and towns around Taihu Lake boast highly-developed silk reeling and weaving industries. Suzhou in Jiangsu, and Huzhou and Hangzhou in Zhejiang are the country's silk industrial centers known far and wide. Suzhou's hand-made embroidery and Hangzhou's picture-weaving in silk are exquisite handicrafts and their products are liked by people from all over the world.

Hilly areas along the Yangtze are producers of subtropical fruits and cash crops. Citrus fruit and tea are two major local products. China is the hometown of tea and silk. The domestic market offers almost countless varieties of tea thanks to a great variety of tea trees grown in the country and different methods used in tea processing. With a warm climate and plentiful rain, areas south of the Yangtze are very suitable for the growth of tea trees and are the biggest tea producer in China. Teas produced in these areas are of high quality. Fa-

Zhoushan fishing port, the biggest in China

mous varieties include Longjing (Dragon Well) produced near Hangzhou's West Lake, Biluochun (green spiral shell-shaped spring tea) produced from hills near Taihu Lake, Yinzhen (silver needle) produced from Junshan Hill in Dongting Lake, and Tunxi green tea and Qimen black tea produced near Anhui's Mount Huangshan.

China is the hometown of porcelain. In history, the middle and lower reaches of the Yangtze were always the country's important porcelain production base. Jingdezhen, Jiangxi Province, produces exquisite porcelain articles and is known as China's "porcelain capital."

Golden Waterways

Cutting through the lower Yangtze encatchment

The Tuotuo River, the source
of the Yangtze

area is a man-made waterway with a long history: the Grand Canal. With a total length of 1,700 km, it starts from Beijing in the north and ends at Hangzhou in the south, running through Hebei, Tianjin, Shandong, Jiangsu and Zhejiang and traversing the five river systems of Haihe, the Yellow River, Huaihe, the Yangtze and Qiantangjiang. In history, it was a golden waterway linking the south and north of the country. Today, the section of the Grand Canal north of the Yellow River has been abandoned, but the other section connecting Shandong, Jiangsu and Zhejiang still plays an important role as an artery of transportation. For example, it serves as an important route for shipping northern coal to south China and southern grain to north China.

In China today, the "golden waterway" honor

goes indisputably to the Yangtze.

The longest river in China, the Yangtze originates from the Jianggendiru Glacier of the snow-capped Geladandong Mountain of the Tanggula Range in Qinghai Province. The river's source section is called Tuotuo River; the next section downstream is called Tongtian River; and further downstream the Yangtze is called Jinsha River. It is not until it reaches the city of Yibin in Sichuan Province that the river is called the Yangtze. With a total length of 6,300 km, the Yangtze is the longest river in Asia and the third longest in the world. Its upper section, from its source to Yichang, Hubei Province, has a length of 4,529 km; its middle section, from Yichang to Hukou, Jiangxi Province, is 931 km long; and its lower section, from Hukou to where it empties into the sea, is 840 km long. The river has an encatchment area of 1.8 million sq. km, more than one-fifth of China's total land area.

The Yangtze has a great number of tributaries and cuts through a vast area with plentiful rainfall.

Morning over the Grand Canal

Qutang Gorge, the uppermost of the famed three gorges of the Yangtze

Every year, it discharges close to one trillion cubic meters of water into the sea, 17.5 times the Yellow River's flow and more than one-third of the total flow of all rivers in the country. The Yangtze's major tributaries number more than 700, of which ten have a flow of 1,000 cubic meters per second each.

The Yangtze is China's transport artery. The combined length of all rivers in China except the Yangtze that are open to navigation is less than one half of the total length of navigational channels of the Yangtze river system. The Yangtze from its estuary to Yibin at its upper section is fit for navigation all the year round. The Yangtze is navigable for ships of more than 10,000 dwt downstream from Nanjing, for ships of more than 5,000 dwt downstream from Wuhan, for ships of more than 3,000 dwt downstream from Yichang, and for ships of 1,500 dwt downstream from Chongqing.

The river's major tributaries are all important routes of transportation. These include Hanjiang, Xiangjiang, Ganjiang, Jialing, Minjiang, Fujiang and Wujiang rivers. The Yangtze's massive capacity of transportation has kept fueling economic development in areas along its banks.

The Yangtze brings troubles as well as benefits. The Yangtze encatchment area is one of the most flood-prone regions in China. This is especially true of the river's middle and lower reaches. Since the beginning of this century, serious flooding has hit the Yangtze valley four times, leaving more than 300,000 people dead and causing incalculable economic losses. How to prevent flooding in the middle and lower reaches of the Yangtze, therefore, has been an important issue confronting the country's water conservancy/control authorities.

The Tiger Leaping Gorge of the Tongtian River, one of the upper sections of the Yangtze

On the other hand, the Yangtze's hydropower is far from being fully exploited. The Yangtze and its major tributaries contain a total of 268 million kw of hydropower resources, one half of the national total and unrivaled anywhere else in the world. Of the river's total hydropower resources, 200 million kw is exploitable. Up to now, however, less than one-tenth of the total has been developed. On the Yangtze itself, only one hydropower station has been constructed -- the Gezhouba near Yichang, Hubei Province, which has an installed generating capacity of 2.715 million kw. With a drop of close to 200 meters, the Three Gorges section of the Yangtze, 200 km long, offers ideal sites for the construction of big hydroelectric stations.

It is precisely on this section that a giant hydroelectric station is being constructed. Sandouping at the Xiling Gorge has been selected as the site for the dam of the Three Gorges Hydroelectric Station. The project consists of the dam, a hydroelectric power station and structures facilitating navigation. The dam, at a height of 185 meters, will create a mammoth reservoir with a storage capacity of 40 billion cubic meters of water. The project is expected to play an important role in flood control down the Yangtze. The Three Gorges Station will be installed with 26 generating sets with a combined capacity of 18.2 million kw and able to generate 84.7 billion kwh of electricity a year, one-ninth of the national total generating capacity at present. Power generated by the station will be supplied to east China and north China in addition to

Wuhan that straddles the Yangtze at its middle section. Picture shows Huanghelou, a well-known ancient building in the city. In the background is the Wuhan Yangtze River Bridge.

Chongqing City, Sichuan Province and central China at short distances. The formation of a large reservoir behind the Three Gorges Dam will fundamentally improve navigational conditions along the Sichuan section of the Yangtze, allowing bigger ships to sail upstream to Chongqing and above and reducing transportation costs.

A fleet of barges on the Yangtze

The Three Gorges Project on the Yangtze is a super-large one designed to play the functions of flood prevention, power generation, navigation and environmental protection. It was formally started in December 1994. The Yangtze was successfully dammed at the project site in November 1997, ending phase one of the project's construction. The Three Gorges Project is scheduled for completion in 2009.

The Yangtze encatchment area plays an important role in the country's economic life. The area has one-third of the national population and one quarter of all the country's farmland; it produces 40% of China's total grain output, one-third of its cotton output and huge quantities of rape seed, silk cocoons, flax, tea and tobacco. Densely-wooded hilly areas along the Yangtze make the river valley the second richest in forest resources in the country, after northeast China. And the valley's cash trees -- producers of tung oil and tea oil -- are known far and wide. Plains in the river valley, China's well-known "land of fish and rice," produce two-thirds of the national output of freshwater fish and are the nation's biggest rice producer. The Yangtze encatchment area is also rich in mineral resources: it ranks first in the world in tungsten and antimony deposits; and its deposits of iron, manganese, copper, coal, petroleum and well salt account for considerable proportions of national totals. Big cities such as Chongqing, Wuhan, Nanjing and Shanghai and countless numbers of medium-sized and small cities along the Yangtze create about 40% of China's GDP.

According to a national development blueprint, the Yangtze Valley, like the nation's coastal corridor, has been slated for priority development now and in the immediate future. A considerable number of ports along the Yangtze have been opened to foreign investment and foreign ships. Many cities along the river have maintained robust economic development in recent years thanks to the river valley's rich produce and transport conveniences provided by the Yangtze. Development of Shanghai's Pudong and construction of the Three Gorges Project, in particular, have been stimulating economic development in the entire Yangtze Valley.

Famous Mountains, Beautiful Scenery

There are many famous mountains in areas south of the Yangtze. They are not particularly tall, but their beauty is a great attraction for domestic and international tourists.

Mount Huangshan, in southern Anhui, is one of the best-known scenic mountains in China. It

Mount Huangshan is known for its strange pines, grotesque stones and lingering mist

has a granite body and its Lianhua and Tiandu peaks rise more than 1,800 meters above sea level. Strange-shaped pine trees, grotesque rocks, hot springs and a sea of mist have been reputed to be the "four stunning features of Mount Huangshan." An ancient Chinese saying reads: "No mountain is worth watching after a trip to the five sacred mountains; and no sacred mountain is worth watching after a trip to Mount Huangshan." Mount Huangshan has been listed by the United Nations Educational, Scientific and Cultural Organization as a World Natural and Cultural Heritage site.

Mount Lushan, in Jiangxi, rises abruptly on the southern bank of the Yangtze, with the vast Poyang Lake lying at a short distance to the east. Waterfalls adorn many slopes of the mountain. A poem by Tang Dynasty poet Li Bai (701-762) reads: "Whiffs of purple vapor rise from the peak of Xianglu under the sun; looked from afar, a waterfall hangs mid-air above a river in front of a slope. Flying waters plunge down three thousand feet; it seems as if the Milky Way had fallen from the Ninth Heaven." Mount Lushan is an important summer resort in the middle reaches of the Yangtze. In summer, when sweltering heat makes life in the nearby cities of Jiujiang and Wuhan miserable, it is as cool as spring at the mountain's Guling peak.

Zhejiang has numerous places of stunning scenery. The Yantang Mountain, the site of an old volcanic mountain, is known for its many abrupt peaks and waterfalls. The Dalongqiu Waterfall plunging 190 meters from the Zilai Peak of the mountain is regarded as a natural wonder. The Qiantang River, which is also called the Fuchun River, has been a source of great natural beauty since ancient times. Along a 100-plus-km section of the river upstream of Tonglu, rugged mountain peaks are reflected in clear, blue water; and waterfalls crash down mountain slopes. In one of his poems, Tang Dynasty poet Bai Juyi (772-846) says of the river: "With the advent of spring, the bluish-green river water turns into a deep blue." Today, a big hydroelectric power station has been built on Xin'anjiang River, a tributary of the Qiantang. Behind the station is a mammoth reservoir dotted with islets -- tips of former low mountain peaks. The enchanting scenery of the man-made lake makes it a great tourist attraction.

Mount Sanqingshan in Jiangxi Province, a Taoist shrine in history

The Wulingyuan scenic area in the mountainous western Hunan Province has a sandstone peak forest terrain that is quite rare in the world. With green mountain peaks and deep ravines, it attracts an increasing number of tourists.The most famous mountain in hilly areas south of the Yangtze is perhaps Mount Hengshan on the west bank of the Xiangjiang River in Hunan Province. On the wooded mountain are numerous places of historical interest, including a temple named after Mount Hengshan.

Mount Wudang in Hubei and Mount Longhu in Jiangxi are well-known Taoist shrines.

The Shanghai-Nanjing-Hangzhou Economic Belt

In the Yangtze Delta, along two railways that connect the cities of Nanjing, Shanghai and Hangzhou lie a number of bustling medium-sized cities such as Wuxi, Zhenjiang, Changzhou, Suzhou, Kunshan and Jiaxing. Recent years have witnessed the rapid emergence of some boom cities on the northern bank of the Yangtze such as Nantong, Yangzhou, Yizheng and Taizhou. Together with Shanghai, Nanjing and Hangzhou, these cities make the Yangtze Delta one of China's most prosperous economic zones.

Shanghai is the country's biggest industrial and commercial city. With a fairly complete range of industries of a fairly long history, the city plays a vital role in the nation's economic life (more about

The Suzhou High- and New-Tech Industrial Development Zone

The port of Lianyungang in Jiangsu Province, the east starting point of the New Eurasia Continental Bridge.

Shanghai below). Hangzhou is not only a world-renown tourist city but also China's foremost silk industrial center. Nanjing is known for its chemical, radio and automotive industries. In the last 30 years, Wuxi and Suzhou, long known for their light and textile industries, have developed themselves into new industrial cities encompassing many areas of production.

To promote economic development along the coast and the Yangtze, Pudong, a Singapore-sized piece of land wedged between Shanghai proper and the East China Sea, has been under development since 1992. The role of Pudong as an economic locomotive for Shanghai, for the Shanghai-Nanjing-Hangzhou economic zone and even for the entire country is beginning to be felt.

Besides, the capital cities of provinces along the

Yangtze, such as Hubei's Wuhan, Jiangxi's Nanchang and Anhui's Hefei, have industries of considerable sizes. For example, Wuhan has developed a sizable iron and steel industry by using locally-produced iron ore, and the city of Shiyan in northwestern Hubei is now home to one of the country's biggest automotive enterprises.

Southwest China

Southwest China comprises Sichuan, Yunnan and Guizhou provinces and Chongqing, a centrally-administered municipality. It borders the Qinghai-Tibet Plateau, the "roof of the world," in the west and is separated from other parts of China by high mountain ranges. It is distinctly different from east China in natural conditions. Southwest China can be divided into two parts: the Sichuan Basin surrounded by tall mountain ranges where the cities of Chengdu and Chongqing are located, and the Yunnan-Guizhou Plateau. Conditions of transportation in southwest China are relatively poor owing to its rugged terrain. Since the founding of New China in 1949, the region's conditions of transportation have improved markedly and the regional economy has had a rapid development. But transportation difficulties continue to restrain economic development in this region.

Landform and Transportation

The fact that the Sichuan Basin is difficult of access has been known far and wide since antiquity, as is proven by this ancient saying: "The road

to Sichuan is more difficult than that to the heavens."

The basin is surrounded by mountains and plateaus on all sides: by the Qinling and Dabashan ranges in the north, the Wushan range in the east, the Hengduanshan range and Qinghai-Tibet Plateau in the west, and the Daloushan range and Yunnan-Guizhou Plateau in the south. These ranges and plateaus, which are huge in size and rise to an average of 1,000-2,000 meters above sea level, constitute barriers between the basin and the heartland of China. Before 1950s, Sichuan had only a 60-km mining railway; its only links with the outside world were several low-grade highways and the dangerous Sichuan section of the Yangtze, called the Chuanjiang.

In landform, the Yunnan-Guizhou Plateau is entirely different from the Inner Mongolia Plateau. It has a rugged terrain interspersed with tall mountain ranges. "It never keeps clear for three consecutive days, nor is there three *li* of land that is flat" is a popular saying that describes conditions in Guizhou. Conditions of transportation in the Yunnan-Guizhou Plateau used to be extremely backward, too. Aside from a narrow-gauge railway that connected Kunming, the provincial capital of Yunnan, with Hanoi in Vietnam, there was no other means of transportation except a few poorly-maintained highways. To get to other parts of China, people in Kunming had to go via Vietnam and the sea.

The Hengduan mountain range is known for its rugged terrain and different climatic conditions at different altitudes.

The Hengduan mountain range that runs from north to south in western Sichuan and Yunnan

To make southwest China more easily accessible, the Chinese government has over the last four decades invested heavily in railway construction in the region. Chronologically, the following have been built: the Chengdu-Chongqing Railway, Baoji-Chengdu Railway, Sichuan-Guizhou Railway (from Chongqing to Guiyang), Hunan-Guizhou Railway (from Zhuzhou to Guiyang), Guiyang-Kunming Railway, Chengdu-Kunming Railway and Xiangfang-Chongqing Railway. Many of them have been electrified. The Nanning-Kunming Railway that opened to traffic in 1997 is a sea-oriented transport artery for southwest China. It starts from Kunming, the provincial capital of Yunnan, and ends at Beihai, a port city in Guangxi, with one section cutting through Guizhou.

Southwest China has made rapid headway in road construction, too. Today, highways link the region with the rest of the country as well as lead

The Sichuan-Tibet Highway

to every county within the region. A number of high-grade highways have been constructed in recent years. The Sichuan-Tibet Highway (from Chengdu to Lhasa) and the Yunnan-Tibet Highway (from Kunming to Lhasa) built over many years after the founding of New China have played an important role in strengthening ties between Tibet and the rest of the country. As road projects, they have few rivals in the world in terms of engineering difficulty. Chengdu, Chongqing, Kunming and Guiyang are each served by a large civilian airport, and air routes connect them with Beijing, other provinces and even foreign cities.

The Sichuan section of the Yangtze, called Chuanjiang, is an important transport route linking Sichuan and Chongqing with the outside world. The river's rapid currents, dangerous shoals and submerged rocks used to inspire fear in boatmen working along the Chuanjiang. This is especially true of the Three Gorges section of the river. In the last four decades, draconian efforts have been made to improve navigational conditions along this section of the river. Sailing on the river section is no longer as dangerous as before, though it continues to be an awe-inspiring experience for the most seasoned sailor. With the construction in the early 1980s of the Gezhouba Hydroelectric Power Station on the Yangtze near the city of Yichang, navigational conditions in the river's Three Gorges section have further improved. Following the completion of the Three Gorges Project on the Yangtze now under construction, there will appear a vast man-made lake stretching from Yichang to Chongqing, turning the present unruly Three Gorges into a placid watery thoroughfare.

Rural scenery in Sichuan Province, southwest China

Land of Plenty

Developed early and at a much higher level than Yunnan and Guizhou, Sichuan has always been known as "A Land of Plenty." Around Chengdu in the western part of the Sichuan Basin is a fertile plain of considerable size. Two thousand years ago, the local people built the Dujiangyan irrigation project on the Minjiang, a tributary of the Yangtze, diverting its water to the Chengdu Plain by natural gravity. The plain has since been immune to both drought and flooding and enjoyed good harvests every year. It is still one of the most developed agricultural areas in the country. Sichuan is both a populous province and a big grain producer.

Owing to differences in landform, the Sichuan Basin is superior in calorific conditions to Hubei, Anhui and Jiangsu located in the same latitudinal area. Approximately the same kinds of crops are grown in these areas, but output in Sichuan is usually greater and more varieties are found there. For example, people in Sichuan can grow such subtropical fruits as litchi and longan, which are usually found in Guangdong, Guangxi and Fujian.

Sichuan is rich in mineral resources, which include iron, coal, natural gas, petroleum and numerous nonferrous metals. The Panzhihua area by the Jinsha River (an upper section of the Yangtze) has the biggest iron deposits in southwest China. The area ranks first in the world in reserves of vanadium and titanium which come associated with iron deposits there. A giant iron and steel works

Chengdu Plain, Sichuan Province, has a well-developed agriculture.

built at Panzhihua now produces nonferrous metals such as vanadium and titanium as well as millions of tons of steel a year. Centering on the mining and smelting of iron ore, Panzhihua, a new, modern industrial city, has emerged in the mountainous area of the same name.

Sichuan is a major natural gas producer. Zigong in the province, a producer of well salt since ancient times, is known as China's "Salt Capital." As early as more than 1,000 years ago, local people began burning natural gas — which they acquired as a result of digging deep wells for brine — in salt production. Natural gas is now being fully developed in the province and used extensively in the chemical industry.

Sichuan ranks first in China in hydropower resources, which are contained in the Jinsha River

— an upper section of the Yangtze — and numerous tributaries of the Yangtze including Dadu, Yalong, Wujiang and Minjiang rivers. Big hydroelectric power stations that have been built are the Gongzui Station on the Dadu River and the Wujiangdu Station on the Wujiang River (in Guizhou). An even bigger station, the Ertan, is now under construction on the Yalong River.

Chongqing — the Economic Center in Southwest China

The centrally-administered Chongqing Municipality was established in 1997. Among the

Jiuzhaigou, or Nine-Stockade Gully, extends 40 km in western Sichuan. It is a great tourist attraction.

country's four centrally-administered municipalities, Chongqing is the youngest but the biggest: it has jurisdiction over 82,000 sq. km and has a population of 30.02 million.

Chongqing is an important transport hub in southwest China: it is the place of convergence for two rivers, the Yangtze and the Jialing, and for three railways linking respectively Chongqing and Chengdu, Chongqing and Xiangfan in Hubei, and Chongqing and Guiyang. Chongqing is also the economic center in southwest China and the upper reaches of the Yangtze. Industry is the mainstay of Chongqing's economy, with car and motorcycle making, chemicals and metallurgical production as its three industrial "pillars." The city's output of motorcycles accounts for one-third of the national total. In recent years, Chongqing has also focused on developing machine-building, electronics and information industries.

Huangguoshu Waterfall, more than 30 meters wide and over 60 meters high, is the biggest in China. It is located in Guizhou Province, southwest China.

Chongqing has rich natural resources. In addition to abundant farm produce and rich water resources, the municipality has deposits of coal, natural gas, iron and other minerals that have industrial values. Chongqing is one of a few big cities in China having achieved self-sufficiency in energy.

Economically, Chongqing has close ties with, and a strong radiating effect on, the rest of southwest China. Within a Chongqing-centered area with a radius of 500 km are: more than 100 million people, three big cities each with a population of more than 2 million, over 30 cities each with a population of more than 300,000, and the Three Gorges Hydroelectric Power Project on the Yangtze, the nation's largest. Bringing into full play the role of Chongqing as a super-large economic center is conducive to accelerated economic and social development in the entire southwest China.

Unique, Colorful *Karst* Terrain

There are large limestone zones in southwest China. Those in Guizhou cover 80% of the province's total land area. Limestone also covers more than half of the land area in the eastern half of Yunnan. A warm and wet climate and long erosion by water have resulted in a widespread *karst* terrain typified by the existence of helictite, stone forests, peak forests, corroded funnel, solution depression, sinkholes, caverns and subterranean rivers. Such landforms represent limestone's different stages of evolution and can be found everywhere in Guizhou and Yunnan. In Yunnan's Lunan

The Yunnan-Guizhou Plateau has a well-developed karst landform. Picture shows a stone forest in Yunnan.

A karst cave in
Guizhou Province

area is a "stone forest" consisting of natural limestone pillars ranging from several to dozens of
meters in height. It is now part of a scenic area for
tourists. The Lijiang River scenic area at Guilin in
Guangxi is another typical karst terrain — peak
forest.

Karst formations have high tourism values.
Aside from the "stone forest" in Yunnan's Lunan
area, the Huangguoshu Waterfall in Guizhou is also
a *karst* phenomenon. The waterfall plunges 60
meters down a hanging cliff, its roaring sound au-
dible from miles away. In fact, Huangguoshu is
but one, albeit the biggest, of a group of waterfalls
in the area, which has high development values.

The limestone region is among the poorest in
China. This is because water escapes easily through
cracks and caverns in *karst* country, making farming there less productive. In recent years, the gov-

ernment has focused its aid-the-poor program on *karst* areas. Within limestone country are solution depressions of considerable size and wide river valleys, which boast highly-developed agriculture and are home to fairly big towns and industrial enterprises. Local people call solution depressions *bazi* (plain), and a large *bazi* can cover more than 100 sq. km of fertile land. They are the cream of *karst* country. Kunming, the capital of Yunnan, and Guiyang, the capital of Guizhou, are located respectively in their provinces' biggest mountain-surrounded basins.

Research and treatment of *karst* not only concerns local economic development but is also an important earth science subject. *Karst* research in China has a long history. In the last years of the Ming Dynasty more than 400 years ago, Xu Xiake, a great Chinese traveler, conducted a series of field investigations into *karst* structures in southwest China. Event today, detailed descriptions of karst structures in Yunnan and Guizhou contained in his "Travel Notes by Xu Xiake" still have important scientific values.

Home to Many Ethnic Minority Groups

Southwest China is home to more than 20 ethnic minority groups, the largest for any region. Of these groups, the Yi and Miao nationalities are the most populous, with each having a population of more than five million. Groups each with a population of more than one million are Bouyei, Dong,

Terraced fields in Yuanyang County, Yunnan Province, southwest China

Bai, Hani and Tibetan. The populations of other groups range from tens of thousands to hundreds of thousands. A few groups are quite small. The Drung nationality, for example, has about 4,000 people only.

Ethnic minority people in Sichuan live mainly in the Hengduan mountainous area in the western part of the province. The Qiangs and Yis there live mainly along river valleys, whereas the Tibetans live on west Sichuan plateaus and have basically the same customs as their brothers and sisters living on the Qinghai-Tibet Plateau.

In Yunnan and Guizhou, several ethnic minority groups usually inhabit a wide area, but each group lives in a compact community. According to a survey, ethnic minority groups live together

Miao women decked out in a traditional way

in about two-thirds of all townships in the two provinces; but within each area with mixed inhabitation, different groups live in relatively separate communities. In accordance with their special lifestyles, some groups live in river valleys, others on mountain slopes and still others on mountain tops — a "staircase"-style geographical distribution.

Ethnic minority groups in the Yunnan-Guizhou Plateau have a long history and unique cultures. Travelers would be intrigued by their lifestyles.

The Miao and Bouyei nationalities in Guizhou, who are relatively well educated, live mainly in the southern part of the province. Embroidery and batik are traditional bread-earning skills respectively for Miao and Bouyei women. Their products enjoy fame at home and abroad for their good workmanship.

In Yunnan, the Naxi, Bai, Hani and Dai nationalities are more populous than others. The Naxi people, who live in the Lijiang area, have their own language and script. *Dongba Jing* (Dongba Scriptures), a voluminous book written in the Naxi language, has high literary and historical values. In history, the Naxi group produced many prominent scholars and specialists.

The Mosuos, a branch of the Naxi nationality, living by Lake Lugu in northern Yunnan, are the only group in China which has still kept traditions of a matriarchal society. Among the Mosuos, marriage is extremely free among the young; a consenting young couple can live together without incurring any disapproval; and married young couples can annul their marriage at will. This is called *azhu* marriage. Children resulting from an *azhu* marriage belong to their mother, with the father having no responsibility whatsoever. Vestiges of the Mosuos' matriarchal society have caught the attention of scholars at home and abroad.

The Bai people live between the Cangshan range

Lugu Lake in northern Yunnan. Inhabitants around the lake still keep some time-honored customs.

and Lake Erhai in Yunnan. More than 1,000 years ago, the Bais established here the state of Nanzhao and the state of Dali, which existed for several hundred years. Symbols of the Bai people's highly-developed culture include the ruins of Taihe City as well as the three pagodas and a State of Nanzhao tablet in Chongsheng Temple — all near the city of Dali today. *Sanyuejie* (literally "March Street") is the Bai people's traditional holiday falling on the third day of the third lunar month. On the day, the Bai people in their holiday best pour into the streets of Dali, where they engage in recreational activities and trade.

The Dai people live in the tropical Xishuangbanna area in the southwestern part of Yunnan, mainly by the Lancang River. They are known for their beautiful dances and interesting lifestyle. Here, rubber and coffee plantations are interspersed with elevated bamboo cottages. The Dai people believe in Hinayana Buddhism and all Dai children spend several years in a monastery as monks. The round-shaped Buddhist pagoda is a most common object in a Dai family. The Dai people celebrate their special new year by sprinkling water on one another as a way of praying for good luck. The day is known as the Water-Sprinkling Festival.

The Hani people live mainly in the Ailaoshan mountainous area and along the Honghe River in southern Yunnan. Neat terraced fields they have built on the slopes of the Ailaoshan Mountain are

Va women busy weaving cloth

Dai women fetching water from a Dai-style well

a well-known sight indicating the Hani people's farming skills.

Protecting Endangered Species and Rain Forests

Southwest China is home to many rare animals and plants. And Yunnan's Xishuangbanna is one of only two areas in China, besides Hainan Island, with tropical rain forests.

The giant panda is a well-known rare animal, China's "national treasure." Fossils indicate that giant pandas had their heyday several million years ago, when they lived in almost all southern provinces. They even ventured as far north as the Zhoukoudian area in Beijing. Climatic changes, especially temperature drops during several ice ages, dramatically reduced the number of giant pandas almost to the verge of extinction. Today, giant pandas live mainly in an area bordering Sichuan, Gansu and Shaanxi, where nature reserves have been established mainly for their protection. One of them, the Wolong Nature Reserve in the mountainous western part of Sichuan Province established in 1975, covers 2,000 sq. km. The nature reserve boasts plenty of rainfall and luxuriant plants and trees. In particular, the arrow bamboo, the giant panda's main food, grows well here, ensuring that the animal has enough to eat. Wolong is now China's nature reserve with the greatest concentration of giant pandas — it is now home to about 100 of them.

The giant panda living in a nature reserve

A single tree makes a forest

The World Wildlife Fund has shown great concern for the protection of the giant panda in China. It has helped establish an observation station in the Wolong Nature Reserve, where Chinese and WWF scientists have been studying the giant panda's living environment, habits and characteristics, reproduction process and population development as well as the effect of human activities on the giant panda, with a view to offering more effective methods for the protection of the animal.

Xishuangbanna is located in southwestern Yunnan with a hot, rainy climate. Tracts of rain forests, rare in China, cover mountain slopes in this area. The Chinese government has established a nature reserve here to protect the rain forests and various precious animals and plants in the forests. Also established in Xishuangbanna is a Tropical Plant Research Institute, where scientists from all over the country devote themselves to protecting, utilizing and studying plants in the area. Also, great efforts have been made over the last few decades to introduce tropical cash crops into Xishuangbanna. The area is now dotted with rubber, cocoa and coffee plantations, which report good economic results.

South China   South China as referred to here comprises Guangdong, Guangxi, Fujian, Hainan, Taiwan, the Hong Kong Special Administrative Region and Macao. Most of the region is located in subtropical and tropical zones, and its natural conditions and culture are distinctly different from those in the middle and lower reaches of the Yangtze.

**A Region with a Long
Outward-Looking History**

In ancient China, this region was regarded as being located in the remote south. In the long process of historical development, it developed some distinct cultural characteristics relative to the rest of the country. Within the region itself, there are cultural differences from area to area. A typical example is a surfeit of local dialects in this region: people in Fujian's Quanzhou-Xiamen area speak a Minnan (southern Fujian) dialect, those in Guangdong's Chaozhou-Shantou area speak a Chaozhou dialect, and those in the Guangzhou area speak Cantonese. People in south China have a long tradition of engaging in foreign trade. Prov-

The Pearl River Delta

inces and regions in south China all have coast-lines of varying lengths. Fujian and Guangdong provinces, in particular, have fine harbors, and Quanzhou and Guangzhou have been China's important foreign trade ports since ancient times. In the Southern Song Dynasty more than 1,000 years ago, Quanzhou had developed into a port of trade with a global reach, attracting businessmen from all over the world. In the meantime, many Chinese began emigrating to southeast Asia. With China's door wide open following the Opium War of 1840-42, more Chinese from south China went abroad to seek a better life. And Chinese emigrants took their local dialects to wherever they settled down. Even to this day, Minnan, Chaozhou and Cantonese dialects are still the common language of overseas Chinese in some countries and regions in the world.

Statistics show that, of all foreigners of Chinese descent around the world, those who can trace their

The Nanling mountain range in northern Guangdong Province is the watershed for the Yangtze and Pearl River systems.

origin to south China (mainly Fujian's Quanzhou, Xiamen and Zhangzhou and Guangdong's Chaozhou, Shantou and Pearl River Delta area) number more than 15 million, more than half of all overseas Chinese. Within south China itself are more than 6 million returned overseas Chinese and their family members. That is why the region is called "the land of overseas Chinese."

Despite living abroad, overseas Chinese love their motherland and their hometowns. They have supported development in their respective hometowns with their hard-earned money. In the 1870s, overseas Chinese from Quanzhou donated money for the construction of a Zhuying Primary School in Quanzhou, one of the earliest schools of a new type in China. Tan Kah-kee, a great patriotic overseas Chinese, founded Jimei School in Xiamen in 1913 and Xiamen University in 1919, both schools having a fairly strong influence at home and abroad. Since 1978 when it began implementing reform and open policies, the Chinese government has established, in south China, the five special economic zones of Shenzhen, Zhuhai, Shantou, Xiamen and Hainan, designated as open cities Fuzhou, Guangzhou, Zhanjiang and Beihai, and opened the Pearl River Delta area and the Xiamen-Zhangzhou-Quanzhou area to foreign investment. South China has absorbed large amounts of investment capital from overseas Chinese as well as from Hong Kong and Taiwan and made great headway in developing an export-oriented economy. The region has been a pioneer in China's opening to the outside world.

Great River in South China

The Pearl River, the longest in south China, consists of three rivers — Xijiang (west river), Dongjiang (east river) and Beijiang (north river), which converge at a wide section close to the sea called the Pearl River Mouth. Compared with the Yangtze and the Yellow river, the Pearl River is short: Xijiang, its longest upper section, has a length of no more than 2,200 km. Located in a tropical zone with an annual precipitation of more than 1,000 mm, the Pearl River has an annual flow of 336 billion cubic meters to rank second among big rivers in China after the Yangtze.

From its source in Yunnan, the Xijiang river flows through Yunnan, Guizhou, Guangxi and

Abrupt peaks are scattered about in a limestone area in central Guangxi region

Guangdong. Joined on its way by Qianjiang and Guijiang rivers, Xijiang swells in flow as it goes eastward and becomes a huge river when it arrives at the Pearl River Mouth. The Hongshui river, which is the upper section of the Qianjiang River, a tributary of Xijiang, contains huge amounts of hydropower resources. In recent years, the state has planned to construct on the Hongshui River 11 hydroelectric power stations with a combined generating capacity of 13.13 million kw and an annual electricity output of more than 53 billion kwh. These stations are: Lubuge, Tianshengqiao One, Tianshengqiao Two, Pingban, Longtan, Yantan, Dahua, Bailongtan, Etan, Qiaogong and Datengxia. So far, three stations — Lubuge, Tianshengqiao One and Dahua--have been built and gone into operation.

The Pearl River has an important tributary, Guijiang, which is also called Lijiang. The source of Lijiang is close to the source of Xiangjiang, a tributary of the Yangtze. During the Qin Dynasty more than 2,000 years ago, local people dug a canal that connected Lijiang and Xiangjiang at where they are closest to each other. Called "Lingqu," the canal in history served as an important transport route between the Yangtze and Pearl river systems. Sections of the canal are still in use today.

The Lijiang River cuts through karst country featuring abrupt peaks on verdant flat land. The best of Lijiang scenery is found along the section of the river downstream from Guilin to Yangshuo.

A giant banyan tree in Yangshuo, Guangxi

Guilin scenery

Riding a boat down the river, one seems to pass through a landscape painting. In the crystal-clear water of the river are moving reflections of green peaks, bamboo groves and farmers' cottages. Two lines in an ancient Chinese poem say of the Lijiang scenery: "The river looks like a green silk girdle, and peaks like emerald hairpins." Guilin is one of the most famous tourist destinations in China and receives millions of tourists from all over the world. "Guilin has the best landscape in the world," a Chinese saying of long standing, is recognized by increasing numbers of people.

Guangzhou and the Pearl River Delta

Guangzhou, located at where the Pearl River empties into the sea, is the biggest city, economic center and the biggest port of foreign trade in the south China region. The Pearl River Delta, the biggest plain in south China, provides the city with a strong material foundation. The Guangzhou Commodities Fair held twice a year here is an important window for China's economic exchanges with the rest of the world.

With green trees and a great variety of flowers all the year round, Guangzhou is reputed to be China's "flower city." Guangzhou has a flourishing commerce and a good industrial foundation. It has well-developed light, textile, food processing and consumer electronics industries and fairly strong machine-building and shipbuilding industries as well. Since China began implementing reform and open policies, Guangzhou has made rapid progress economically. Around Guangzhou are numerous medium-sized and small cities boasting vibrant economies. Of them, the special economic zones of Shenzhen and Zhuhai have had the fasttly

Guangzhou, the biggest city in the Pearl River Delta and an important foreign trade port

est economic development.

The Pearl River Delta, with plenty of heat and well-developed irrigation facilities, has been the richest and most populous area in south China since ancient times. Local people raise fish in ponds and grow around them sugar-canes, subtropical fruit and mulberry trees to raise silkworms. Every year, farmers dig up fertile mud from these ponds to nourish what they grow and put silkworm droppings and sugar-cane leaves into the ponds as fish feed. This benign ecological process is called "pond agriculture," which has the advantages of being highly productive and highly efficient, and has won plaudits from ecologists at home and abroad for its economic and ecological benefits. In the Pearl River Delta, farmers harvest silkworm cocoons eight times a year, most for export.

Yuniu Peak of the Wuyi mountain range in Fujian Province

Taiwan and Hainan

Of China's 33 provinces, autonomous regions and centrally-administered municipalities, only Taiwan and Hainan are islands, off the mainland.

Taiwan Province comprises Taiwan Island, Penghu Islands and nearby islands including the Diaoyu Island. With an area of 36,000 sq. km, Taiwan is China's biggest island shaped like a spindle and running largely parallel with the coastline of the mainland. A mountain range with an average height of 2,000 meters above sea level runs the whole length of the island and is the island's watershed. West of the range, the terrain slopes gently with an alluvial plain lying along the coast. It is here that most big and medium-sized cities in Taiwan are located. The eastern side of the mountain range is predominantly steep and precipitous and extends right down to the Pacific.

Taiwan has a warm and wet climate. Except for mountainous areas, the island's annual average temperature exceeds 20°C and precipitation reaches more than 2,000 mm. At Huoshaoliao located in the northeast of the island, the annual precipitation reaches 6,572 mm, the most in all of China. Taiwan has thriving vegetation, with a forest coverage rate of more than 70%. Main crops grown in the island are rice and sugar-cane, and it exports large quantities of rice and sugar every year. That is why Taiwan is known as "a granary" and "a sugar warehouse." Taiwan is also a big producer of subtropical fruits such as pineapple, banana and citrus fruit.

In the 1960s, taking advantage of the second international transfer of labor-intensive industries, Taiwan adopted an export-oriented industrializa-

Fish ponds lined with mulberry trees in the Pearl River Delta

tion strategy and established export-oriented processing zones in Kaohsiung, Nantsu and Taichung to attract foreign investment and develop light and textile industries. In the 1970s, Taiwan shifted the focus of its investment onto infrastructure facilities such as highways, railways and airports as well as basic industries such as iron and steel making, petrochemicals, shipbuilding and power generation. During the ten years from 1963 to 1972, Taiwan's economy grew at an annual average rate of about 10%. In the 1980s, Taiwan further adjusted its economic structure by developing technology-intensive industries. It has developed the Hsinchu Science-Based Industrial Park and made remarkable progress in the manufacturing of high-tech products.

The Tropic of Cancer marker in Taitung, Taiwan

Taiwan has been an inalienable part of Chinese territory since ancient times. People on both sides of the Taiwan Straits long for an early peaceful reunification of their motherland.

Hainan Province comprises Hainan Island and numerous islands in the South China Sea. With an area of 34,000 sq. km, Hainan is China's second biggest island and is separated from Guangdong Province's Leizhou Peninsula by the Qiongzhou Strait. With a width of 18 nautical miles, the Qiongzhou Strait is the link not only between Hainan Island and the mainland but also between the Beibu Gulf and the South China Sea. In wide sea areas to the east and south of Hainan are scattered many islands, sand cays, submerged reefs and submerged banks, of which more than 260 come under Chinese sovereignty and are called collectively Nanhai Islands. Geographically, Nanhai Islands are divided into the four archipelagoes of Dongsha, Xisha, Zhongsha and Nansha and Huangyan Island located east of the Zhongsha Archipelago. The Zengmu Shoal, the southernmost part of Nanhai Islands, lies at latitude 4 degrees north. Nanhai Islands are China's southernmost territory.

Hainan, located in the tropical zone, is suitable for the growth of tropical crops and trees. A great variety has been introduced into Hainan from abroad over the years. Today, more than 400,000 hectares of land are devoted to the cultivation of tropical trees and crops, mainly rubber, coconut, pepper, cashew, lemongrass, sisal hemp, areca, pineapple, coffee, oil palm and cocoa. Hainan is China's biggest rubber production base, its output making up more than two-thirds of the national total. Sea areas around Nanhai Islands are important tropical fishing grounds. Another important product of Hainan is iron ore from Shilu with an iron content of more than 60%, an important raw material for iron and steel enterprises on the mainland.

Hainan Island used to be under the jurisdiction of Guangdong Province. In 1988, it became Hainan Province with Haikou as its capital and was designated at the same time as a special economic zone. In fact, it is the biggest of the country's five SEZs. Hainan's economic development has since entered a new phase.

Hong Kong and Macao

Hong Kong, located to the east of the Pearl River Estuary of Guangdong Province, is composed of Hong Kong Island, Kowloon and the New Territories. It has a total land area of 1,092 sq. km and a population of more than 6.3 million at present, of whom 98% are Chinese. The sea area between Hong Kong Island and Kowloon Peninsula is one of the world's finest natural harbors able to accommodate many giant ships at the same time.

Sun Moon Lake, Taiwan

Hainan Island

Hong Kong is small, densely populated and has limited natural resources. It relies on imports for fuel, industrial raw materials and most foodstuffs. Even fresh water is supplied by the neighboring Guangdong. Hong Kong plays an important role in world economic activities. Trade, finance, commerce, tourism and manufacturing are its economic mainstay. Hong Kong is a world financial center and a free port. A considerable proportion of the mainland's imports and exports gets through Hong Kong.

Hong Kong was occupied by Britain after the Opium War of 1840-42. On July 1, 1997, the Chinese government resumed the exercise of sovereignty over Hong Kong and established there the Hong Kong Special Administrative Region. In accordance with the principle of "one country, two systems," Hong Kong's previous social and economic systems have remained unchanged, the lifestyle of its people has remained unchanged, and laws previously in force there have remained basically unchanged.

Macao, located on the southern side of the Pearl River Estuary, is composed of Macao Peninsula and two nearby islets. It has a land area of 23.5 sq. km and a population of more than 400,000. Gambling used to be Macao's economic mainstay but the last decade has seen a fairly rapid development of industry, foreign trade and tourism, which have claimed a rising proportion in the region's economy.

Macao was occupied by Portugal in the 1550s. In a joint declaration they signed on April 13, 1987, the Chinese and Portuguese governments announced that the Chinese government will resume the exercise of sovereignty over Macao on December 20, 1999.

Hong Kong, located to the east of the Pearl River, is a world-renown free port

2. 2 The Northwest Interior Region

This region comprises Gansu Province and three autonomous regions: Inner Mongolia, Ningxia and Xinjiang. There is an annual 200mm precipitation isogram on China's rainfall map. West of this isogram is a dry area -- the Northwest Interior Region. Here, livestock farming replaces agriculture as the economic mainstay, and the area is home to China's various ethnic minority groups devoted to livestock farming.

Aridity, scant vegetation and vast territory but scarce population are the main features of this region. However, vast deserts, the endless Gobi, lush grasslands and hospitable ethnic minority groups engaged in livestock farming have great appeal to tourists. With rich natural resources, northwest China has great potential for future development.

The Great Deserts

Deserts in China cover an area of 700,000 sq. km. With more than 500,000 sq. km of Gobi added, deserts in the country cover 1.28 million sq. km, 13% of China's total land area. About 80% of all deserts in China are concentrated in arid northwest China. Major deserts include Taklimakan and Gurban Tunggut in Xinjiang, Badain Jaran and Tengger in Inner Mongolia, and Kumutage between Xinjiang and Gansu.

Taklimakan is the largest desert in China and one of the largest in the world. Lying within the Tarim Basin in southern Xinjiang, it covers 337,000 sq. km, close to one half of the total area of deserts in China. Taklimakan is also the driest desert in the country -- annual precipitation there is less than 50 mm. The desert is covered by huge sand dunes except for some low, barren hills on its western fringes. The sand dunes are shaped like a crescent moon, a pyramid, a long ridge, etc. and lie in regular rows according to the local perennial wind direction. Viewed from above, the sand dunes look like sea waves. Not a single well-grown plant or running animal can be found in the desert owing to its extremely hostile natural conditions. In summer, a scorching sun makes life here unbearable; in winter and early spring, sandstorms that darken the sky hold sway. Taklimakan means "one can enter but not come out" in Uygur language.

In arid northwest China with vast deserts, natural vegetation is sparse in most areas.

Gurban Tunggut Desert, located in the Junggar Basin in northern Xinjiang, is the second largest in area in China. Natural conditions there are slightly better than in the Taklimakan: there are tracts of sacsaouls, a drought-resistant tree.

Deserts in the eastern part of northwest China are generally smaller in size and natural conditions there are better. These include Mu Us and Lesser Tengger in Inner Mongolia, where precipitation is greater than in deserts in the western part and where grow drought-resistant grass and wormwood varieties. Shrub-like trees grow in low-lying areas between sand dunes. There are also lakes -- rare sources of water for herdspeople.

Many ruins of ancient cities are buried in the deserts. Early in this century, Sven Anders Hedin, a Swede, and later many domestic expedition teams went into the Taklimakan. Their purpose was to look for ancient cities and cultural relics buried in

Desert scene

the sands. Thanks to a dry climate in desert areas, cultural relics in the ancient cities such as bamboo slips (used for writing on in ancient times), paper, articles of daily use and human bodies in graves are generally well preserved.

After years of comprehensive sand-control efforts, the desert is beginning to recede at Shapotou, Ningxia.

The most interesting are the elusive Lake Lop Nur and the ancient city state of Loulan near the lake. A Russian adventurer once came close to Lake Lop Nur and saw a limitless expanse of water in the desert. But when others came to the same place soon after, they found the lake gone. That is why Lake Lop Nur is also called a "roaming lake." The ancient city of Loulan was recorded in Chinese history, but it mysteriously disappeared around the 11th century. All these have attracted great interest from foreign scientists as well as Chinese scholars.

Under the deserts are rich mineral deposits. Huge oil deposits have been discovered in the two vast deserts located respectively in the southern and northern parts of Xinjiang. In the 1950s, Chinese scientists found petroleum at Karamay on the periphery of the Gurban Tunggut Desert. In recent years, more petroleum has been discovered in the Taklimakan Desert, where total deposits are estimated to exceed 10 billion tons and where oil exploration and development has been in full swing. A highway that runs from the desert fringe to an oilfield in the heart of the desert has been open to traffic. The desert is China's important source of crude oil in the 21st century.

Desertification is a serious problem for China. In history, much farmland and many towns on the fringes of deserts disappeared before encroaching sand dunes. Like the city state of Loulan, Tongwan, the capital city of the ancient state of Western Xia on the Ordos Steppe, was buried by shifting sand dunes. The city lay originally at the heart of a lush grassland but, in the Song Dynasty more than 1,000 years ago, the city and its surrounding area had become desert.

Desertification has created a host of troubles. Drifting sand piles up on newly-built railways and highways, forcing them to stop functioning; and it buries crops to deprive farmers of any harvest. To prevent desertification, Chinese scientists have conducted a lot of relevant investigations and studies in deserts and established experiment stations in some desertification-prone areas. For example, a comprehensive sand-fixing system built along some Ningxia sections of the Baotou-Lanzhou Railway has successfully stayed large tracts of sand

dunes, ensuring the smooth operation of the railway. Construction of the system was based on studies and experiments conducted by scientists.

Geological prospecting has led to discoveries of rich oil

Besides vast deserts, there are in northwest China large tracts of grassland totaling about 300 million hectares. Grassland in Inner Mongolia is not only vast -- it accounts for one-third of the national total, but also good in quality. With well-developed livestock farming, Inner Mongolia is a main supplier of animal products.

The Inner Mongolia Steppe extends from the western slopes of the Greater Hinggan Mountain Range in the east, to the Yinshan Mountain Range and the Great Wall in northern Shaanxi in the south, and to the Sino-Mongolian border in the north. The land is flat except for a few low mountains at its

Folk Customs on the Grassland

eastern fringes and in its interior. Viewed from above, the Inner Mongolia grassland is like a vast sea with endless waves of grass. Herds of cattle, sheep and goats are scattered about all over the grassland. An ancient folk song sings: "The firmament is high, and the grassland is endless. As a wind blows by, the lowered grass reveals grazing cattle and sheep." This is an authentic picture of the vast grassland in Inner Mongolia.

In Inner Mongolia, the best pastureland is found in the Hulun Buir Grassland and Xilin Gol Grassland, where livestock farming is most developed as a result. They are home to the Mongolian horse known far and wide for its great physical stamina and ability to travel long distances. Trained Mongolian horses, docile but full of valor and rigor, can serve as ideal military horses. The Sanhe horse, an improved variety of the Mongolian horse, is even better: it is high and big, has a dark-red color, and is beautifully shaped. It is good at both traveling long distances and carrying heavy loads. Most Mongolian and Sanhe horses come from the Hulun Buir and Xilin Gol grasslands.

Sheep is one of the main animals raised in Inner Mongolia grasslands, and the main variety is the Mongolian Sheep which people raise for both wool and meat. And the best Mongolian Sheep is called the Wuzhu Muqin sheep, which has a high yield of very tender mutton, the first choice for Beijing restaurants serving Mongolian hot pot (Mongolian hot pot is a culinary delight whereby

Ningxia's Tanyang sheep are known far and wide for their fine sheepskin.

Pastureland in Altai Mountains in Xinjiang

customers dip thin slices of mutton briefly in boiling water in a hot pot and eat the mutton with a specially-prepared sauce). Tanyang and Sanbei sheep, bred from the Mongolian sheep, are fine sheepskin varieties. Fur coats made of Tanyang and Sanbei sheepskins are light, soft and warm and are an important export product.

Alxa Grassland is located in the westernmost part of Inner Mongolia. Being farther away from the sea, natural conditions there are harsh with little rain. The area is sparsely covered with thorn-like shrubs. The camel is the main animal in this area. Camels in China are of the two-hump variety and have a strong adaptability to natural conditions. They are local people's means of transportation in endless deserts.

Mongolians (also called Mongols) are the main inhabitants of grasslands in Inner Mongolia. Of the more than 3.40 million Mongolians, over half live in Inner Mongolia with others spread across provinces and regions in northwest China.

The Mongolian nationality is among the fairly old ethnic minority groups in China. Their bravery and valor were well known in world history as well as in Chinese history. In the late 12th century to the early 13th century, Tiemuzhen (1162-1227), born of a Mongolian aristocratic family, conquered other tribes on the Mongolian steppe and established a unified Mongolian khanate. He was given the title of Genghis Khan. Later, the Mongolian khanate sweeping southward subjugated the states of Jin and Southern Song and established in China a Mongolian empire, the Yuan Dynasty (1206-1308), with Dadu (present-day Beijing) as its capital.

Mongolians have a long history and rich cultural heritage. From ancient times to the present, the ethnic group has nurtured a considerable number of famous scientists and scholars, who have left behind works of high value. *A Secret History of the Mongols* (meng gu mi shi), written in the

Hulun Buir is one of the best grasslands in China.

middle of the 13th century, is a representative piece of works recording the history of the Mongolian nationality. Mongolian medicine with rich practical experience is an important part of traditional Chinese medicine. Mongolian dances, bold and unrestrained, have a unique style of their own among Chinese folk dances.

Camels are a major livestock in the desert areas of the Inner Mongolia Steppe with scant rainfall and little vegetation.

Mongolians have their unique customs and habits. They live in yurts, which are round in shape and of different sizes. Usually, each is four meters across and two meters tall. It consists of a wooden framework and a felt cover. A window at the top of the yurt lets in light as well as works for ventilation. A stove sits at the center of the yurt ground. Yurts are easily disassembled, moved and reassembled.

The most important traditional festival for Mongolians is the Nadam Fair held in July or August every year. Nadam in Mongolian means "recreation" and "game playing." On the day of the Nadam Fair on the grassland, Mongolian herdspeople from as far as 100 km away, clad in their holiday best, taking food and their yurts as well as their family members, and traveling by horse or carts, would gather at the fair ground. The fair ground becomes a beehive of activities. Wrestling is the most interesting entertainment at the Nadam Fair. Wrestlers -- strong Mongolian men wearing traditional clothes -- sing songs as they enter the wrestling ground. Horse racing is also very popular.

Inner Mongolia is China's first minority nationality autonomous region. After the founding of New China in 1949, life of the Mongolian people has greatly improved. The state has encouraged herdspeople to settle down instead of moving about and helped them improve their grassland and livestock with financial aid. The capital of Inner Mongolia is Hohhot situated at the foot of the Yinshan Range. After half a century of development, Hohhot has become a prosperous, high-skylined city.

Oasis Agriculture

The dry Northwest China is home to large tracts of deserts and the Gobi, but not all areas in this vast region are barren, devoid of greenery. In this region is distributed a number of high mountain ranges such as the Qilianshan in Gansu and the Tianshan, Kunlun and Altai in Xinjiang. At an average height of more than 2,000 meters above sea level, these mountain ranges are natural barriers that intercept high-altitude wet currents. That is why precipitation is far greater in almost all tall mountains in northwest China. Precipitation can reach 500-600 mm a year in some mountainous areas -- almost the same as that in north China. With low temperatures, less evaporation and great humidity in the air, mountain slopes in northwest China are suitable for the growth of trees and grass. As a result, there are dense forests and lush pastureland in these mountainous areas. Rainfall at tall mountains often comes in the form of snow, and snow accumulated at mountain tops over thousands of years forms giant glaciers. The glaciers, moving slowly down ravines, become gurgling streams and rivers below the snow line. Out of the mountains, these streams and rivers create oasis belts that extend hundreds of kilometers at the foot of the mountains and the edges of deserts. The better-known of these are the oasis belt at the northern foot of the Qilian Range, the two oasis belts respectively at the northern and southern sides of the Tianshan Range, and the oasis belt at the southern foot of the Kunlun Range. The oases are a land of lush greenery, with crisscrossing roads and bustling communities.

People of all ethnic groups who live here, besides growing wheat and other grain crops, have developed a horticulture with strong local characteristics. The seedless grape, Hami melon and other fine fruit varieties they cultivate have a high repu-

An oasis

tation at home and abroad.

A short car ride westward from Gansu Province takes one into Turpan known far and wide as a producer of fine grapes. Turpan is a depression, whose lowest point -- Lake Aiding -- is 155 meters below sea level, the second lowest in the world. The Turpan Depression, located in interior China, is known as "a place of fire." It is extremely dry there with an annual precipitation of less than 10 mm; and it is unbearably hot in summer with average daily temperature reaching 37-38 degrees Celsius. But right at the edge of this hostile basin lies an oasis, Turpan Oasis, which owes its existence to accumulated snow at the top of the Tianshan Mountain Range. When summer comes, the snow and ice on the mountain top melt and become torrential water, bringing life to this otherwise barren land.

Turpan is well known for its fine grapes and Hami melons having a high sugar content. Turpan grapes and melons are highly valued in particular since they are typical "green food:" they are not contaminated by pesticides as, growing in dry and hot desert, they are free of diseases and insect pests. Perhaps that is why they sell well on the international market.

To make full use of available water by reducing evaporation, the local people have invented a unique water-diversion way called karez -- an irrigation system of wells connected by underground channels.

Water flows out of a karez, an irrigation system of wells connected by underground channels, in Xinjiang.

Turpan has large-scale karez systems: the number of underground irrigation channels reaches more than 1,000 with a total length of over 3,000 km. The amount of water diverted annually exceeds 600 million cubic meters, which irrigates 80% of Turpan farmland. The karez is a great invention and, like the Grand Canal, a great water engineering project.

Glaciers play an important role in supplying water to rivers and sustaining oases in arid northwest China.

In addition to Turpan oasis, there are in northwest China Zhang Ye, Wuwei and Jiuquan oases in Gansu Province, Shihezi oasis in northern Xinjiang, and Korla, Aksu, Kashi and Hetian oases in southern Xinjiang.

The Uygurs, with a population of six million, form the third biggest ethnic minority group in China after the Zhuangs and Huis. The majority of them live in Xinjiang, predominantly in oases in southern Xinjiang. The Uygurs have a long history: they are the descendants of the ancient Huihe group, which in the eighth century established a Huihe khanate pledging allegiance to the Táng Dynasty. During the hundreds of years when they lived in Xinjiang, Huihes mixed together with the local Hans and members of other ethnic groups to become today's Uygur Nationality. The Uygurs are engaged mainly in irrigated agriculture, producing wheat, rice, corn, cotton, flax and various kinds of fruits and melons.

The Uygurs are born good traders. Their ancestors lived along the ancient Silk Road and generations of Uygurs were engaged in commerce. Aside from selling their produce on the market, they make exquisite woolen products such as carpets and *gaba*, a four-cornered embroidered cap traditionally worn by the Uygurs. The *gaba* is also well liked by foreign tourists. In Hetian at the foot of the Kunlun Mountains, local Uygurs make famous jade carvings from locally-produced Hetian jade.

With economic reform now geared to the establishment of a market economy in China, Uygurs' commercial activities have become even more active. Kashi, the commercial center of southern Xinjiang located on the east side of the Pamirs,

Pastureland in Tianshan Mountains in the central Asian region of Xinjiang

is becoming increasingly prosperous with trade. One of the city's tourist attractions is the bazaar, where countless traders' stalls sell handicraft articles, fruit and melons as well as general merchandise.

Xinjiang is home to Hans, Kazaks, Huis and Kirgizs in addition to Uygurs. Kazaks, a straightforward people, like wrestling and a game called *diaoyang* (a sheep-snatching competition on horseback); and all Kazaks, old and young, male and female, are good at horse riding. Kirgizs are a hospitable people: they treat guests with the best they have and offer mutton from the sheep head to their most respected guests.

A lamb-grabbing contest among Kazak herdsmen

The Silk Road

The Silk Road refers to a busy trade route in ancient times that extended westward from Chang'an (present-day Xi'an), cut through eastern Gansu and the Gansu Corridor, passed through the Yumen and Yangguan passes, traversed Xinjiang, central Asia and western Asia and ended in Europe. The route is so named because Chinese silk was a major commodity it was used to transport. In history, the Silk Road repeatedly changed its route; also, it had more than one route. And silk was not the only commodity transported on the Road. In fact, the Silk Road is a general term for a land transportation route extending from China to Europe. As a link of economic and cultural exchanges between China and the West, the Silk Road has an important place in the history of world civilization.

The Silk Road within China can be divided into three sections: the eastern section, from Chang'an to Wuwei in Gansu; the middle section coinciding with the Gansu Corridor; and the western section, that cuts through Xinjiang. The Silk Road was opened in the Western Han Dynasty 2,000 years ago. Zhang Qian, an emissary of Emperor Wudi of the dynasty, traveled to *xiyu* (literally, "western regions," which are present-day central Asia) several times and succeeded in bringing many city states there under the jurisdiction of Western Han. And this opened a trade route that was to traverse Eurasia. By the Tang Dynasty (618-907), the Silk Road had become unprecedentedly busy. An entry in a historical record says: "There is an endless stream of traders and emissaries on the road." The Silk Road promoted economic development in areas it passed through, with towns and cities emerging by the roadside. These include Wuwei, Zhangye, Jiuquan and Dunhuang in the Gansu Corridor, all bustling cities. The Silk Road played an important role in promoting cultural and economic exchanges between China and countries and regions to its west. The Road made it possible for the following Chinese products and skills to spread westward: silk, jade articles, iron tools, various kinds of handicraft articles, the cultivation of peaches, plums and apricots, sericulture, iron smelting and papermaking. It also made it possible for foreign plants and products to spread to China such as cotton, grape, alfalfa, pomegranate, walnut, sesame, watermelon, glass and woolen fabric. India's Buddhism also spread to China via the Silk Road, exerting far-reaching influences over the Chinese culture.

The Silk Road served as a busy east-west link for more than 1,000 years. During this period, peoples of different countries along this Road created splendid cultures. Countless objects of historical interest and cultural relics preserved along the Road are silent testimony to its bygone prosperity.

Stone caves are among the most intriguing cultural heritages along the Silk Road. Within China are Mogao Caves at Dunhuang (Gansu), Bingling Temple Caves at Yongjing (Gansu), Maijishan Caves at Tianshui (Gansu), and Kezier Caves at

Moving herds up and down mountain slopes of different altitudes in search of pastureland in Xinjiang as seasons change

Baicheng (Xinjiang). Mogao Caves at Dunhuang are the best among China's four best-known cave sites (the others are Yungang Caves at Datong, Longmen Caves at Luoyang, and Maijishan Caves at Tianshui). Mogao Caves extending over a length of two kilometers are located at the foot of Mount Mingsha 25 km southeast of the county seat of Dunhuang County, Gansu Province. Existing today at Mogao are: 492 caves, more than 45,000 sq. meters of murals and over 2,400 colored sculptured Buddhist statues. Toward the end of the 19th century, huge amounts of ancient Buddhist scriptures, documents and paintings were discovered in a sealed stone cave at Dunhuang. Scientists have since conducted uninterrupted studies of them as well as Mogao caves themselves and, gradually, a new international science discipline has come into being: Dunhuangology. Unfortunately, some of the discovered items are missing or damaged and some precious items have been plundered by foreign countries.

The Silk Road gradually declined after the Tang Dynasty and was later abandoned. This is due to

The Gansu Corridor along the length of which the ancient Silk Road extended westward is site to numerous places of historical interest. Dunhuang's Mogao Caves are located at the western end of the Corridor.

several reasons: a gradual southward shift of China's economic center, the emergence of marine transport, and westward campaigns by the Mongols of the Yuan Dynasty that devastated economies and cultures in central Asia.

Fruits and melons produced in Xinjiang are known for their superior quality

Today, great changes have taken place along the Silk Road. Running parallel to the ancient Silk Road, the Lanzhou-Xinjiang Highway and the Lanzhou-Xinjiang Railway have connected cities of fame along the Silk Road as well as northwest China with the rest of the country. Oases along the Silk Road have kept expanding in area and produce more grain than local people can consume as well as fruits and melons that are sold throughout China. Lanzhou, the provincial capital of Gansu, located on the Silk Road, is northwest China's big-

Ruins of the once prosperous
Yumen Pass on the Silk Road

gest industrial city, transport hub and cultural center. The ancient city of Jiuquan on the Road is home to northwest China's biggest steel works. China's biggest nickel mine and nickel smelting base have emerged at Jinchang in the heart of the Gobi Desert. The Yumen Oilfield near the Yumen Pass, a communications hub in ancient times, is China's oldest petroleum production base.

Desert sights and numerous places of historical interest along the Silk Road are a great tourist source. Sightseeing along the Silk Road is one of the most attractive tourist items offered by China's travel agencies. The double-tracking of the Lanzhou-Xinjiang Railway that runs from Lanzhou to Urumqi, the capital of Xinjiang, a project completed in 1996, has increased transport capacity in northwest China. In 1992, a new Eurasia continental bridge that starts from the port of

Lianyungang, Jiangsu Province, in the east and ends at Rotterdam in the Netherlands in the west opened to traffic. In the first leg of transportation, Asia-Pacific region-sourced cargoes bound for countries in central Asia, western Asia and Europe arrive at Lianyungang via the sea, are loaded onto rail cars and transported to the Ala Pass on the Chinese-Kazakhstan border via the Chinese section of the continental bridge -- the Longhai Railway (from Lianyungang to Lanzhou) and the Lanzhou-Xinjiang Railway; entering Kazakhstan, the cargoes are then reloaded and hauled to their different destinations via five routes. Naturally, cargoes can also go in the reverse direction. This new Eurasia continental bridge has become the most economical and direct international transport route linking Asia and Europe.

Highways and a railway have now replaced ancient camel caravans to link the Gobi with the outside world.

2.3
The Qinghai-Tibet Plateau

The Qinghai-Tibet Plateau, the highest and youngest plateau in the world, is known as "the roof of the world." The Kunlun and Qilian mountain ranges lie in its northern part; the Himalayas, the highest mountain range in the world, in its southern part; the Hengduan range in its eastern part; and the Pamirs in its western part. The plateau minus the tall mountain ranges has an average elevation of more than 4,000 meters above sea level. Scattering around the plateau are high mountainous areas, gentle valleys and basins. The Qinghai-Tibet Plateau is home to two provincial-level administrative regions: Qinghai Province and Tibet Autonomous Region. Qinghai, located in the northeastern part of the plateau, is the smaller of the two. The western part of Qinghai is a dry inland basin -- the Qaidam. The rest of the plateau is Tibet where Tibetans are the main inhabitants. In fact, the Qinghai-Tibet Plateau is Tibetans' native place. Tibetans, who live in a high-altitudinal, snow-dominated environment, have their unique lifestyle and have developed a culture characteristic of such a lifestyle.

The Roof of the World

The rise of the Qinghai-Tibet Plateau has always received attention from earth scientists at home and abroad. Some scientists assert that studying the formation and formation mechanism of the Qinghai-Tibet Plateau can bring about a revolution in geoscience. Research results released so far indicate that the Qinghai-Tibet Plateau used to be a vast sea and that, two million years ago, there was no Qinghai-Tibet Plateau. Later, several earth crust uplifts of considerable magnitude brought this barren, cold plateau into being.

According to plate tectonics, a fairly prevalent theory, the Qinghai-Tibet Plateau has resulted from the rise of earth crust caused by the collision of the Indian Plate and the Eurasia Plate. To find proof of the collision of the two plates, scientists have conducted many field surveys on the Qinghai-Tibet Plateau. They have found that rocks of the Himalayas Mountain Range on the southern periphery of the plateau contain large amounts of ancient marine life and that there are in the Yalu Zangbu River Valley north of the Himalayas a considerable number of special rocks having resulted from earth crust squeezing. These are evi-

Chayu south of the Himalayas is a fertile area in Tibet.

dences for study and inference by scientists.

Emergence of the Qinghai-Tibet Plateau has brought about big climatic changes to the world, to east Asia in particular. Within the plateau itself, from the Holocene epoch about 10,000 years ago to the present, owing to the rise of the plateau, a fairly humid and warm climate gradually gave way to a cold and dry one, and large lakes that originally existed on the plateau shrank in size and disappeared. The rise of the plateau has also changed atmospheric circulation, resulting in a stronger east Asia monsoon, drier climate in the western half of China, and an increasingly distinct monsoon climate in its eastern half.

Up to now, the Qinghai-Tibet Plateau is still an area with intense earth crust activities. In the interior of the plateau are countless hot springs, in-

Mount Qomolangma, the highest peak of the Himalayas

Scenery on the Qinghai-Tibet Plateau

cluding geysers that give spectacular sights. Seismic activities are quite frequent at the eastern periphery of the plateau. In the 1950s, an extremely violent earthquake hit the Chayu area in southeastern Tibet. Scientists have also discovered that the Himalayas keeps rising, at a rate of about several millimeters a year.

Plateau Landscape

The Qinghai-Tibet Plateau has a typical plateau climate: strong radiation from the sun, low temperatures, thinner air with a lower oxygen content in the atmosphere, compared with low-altitude areas. As soon as you alight from your aircraft at the Lhasa Airport, you immediately feel short of breath, giddy and dizzy; your heart beats faster than usual. These are typical symptoms of mountain sickness caused by thinner air. You will also find that sunshine in Lhasa has a stronger dazzle, and that the sky there is bluer, than anywhere else. These are natural features of a plateau.

If you go into Tibet via Qinghai by car, you

will be taken away by what you see along the way. You will pass through a vast, barren area. Your vehicle can travel hundreds of kilometers without a single person being seen. All you see are snow-capped mountains, an endless expanse of barren land and, occasionally, several yaks grazing on low grass.

Natural conditions on the Qinghai-Tibet Plateau are extremely hostile. The vast area is subject to frequent howling winds and violent weather changes. Animals and plants on the plateau have acquired unique properties that are adapted to such an environment. Plants there have a relatively short stalk and a short growing period; they are usually covered with a thick layer of cutin or fine-haired epidermis to resist strong sunshine, low tempera-tures and fierce winds; and they have a well-de-veloped root system against long drought bouts. For animals on the plateau, the most striking fea-

The Yarlung Zangbo River cutting through the Himalayas

tures are well-developed heart and lungs, big vital capacity, and a much higher haemoglobin content in the their blood than in the blood of the same animals living on low-lying plains. These characteristics allow the animals to live normally in a low-oxygen environment.

The most common plant on the Qinghai-Tibet Plateau is a low grass called Tibet Kobresia, which local Tibetans call "butter grass." It covers almost the entire Qinghai-Tibet Plateau and, viewed at a distance, tracts of land covered with the grass look like green carpets. Tibet Kobresia, rich in nutrition, is the best forage grass for the Tibetan sheep. The Tibetan sheep and the yak are the main domestic animals on the plateau. The yak, covered with long, dense hairs, is cold-resistant and extremely strong. It is called "boat on the plateau."

The Qinghai-Tibet Plateau is dotted with numerous large lakes with clear water. Land around the lakes, which is mostly flat, with plenty of water, slightly high temperatures and better vegetation than elsewhere on the plateau, is often the best pastureland for Tibetan herdsmen. In comparatively low-lying areas in and along the Yalu Zangbu river valley in southern Tibet, where temperatures are higher than elsewhere, local people grow highland barley, wheat and pulses. Thanks to strong sunshine, individual crops can have a high yield. For example, individual potatoes can weigh more than half a kg each and individual carrots 2-3 kg each. The state has given much attention to

Herd-caring Tibetan girl

Tibet's agriculture. An agricultural research institute has been established in Lhasa, the regional capital; and much headway has been made in the introduction of crops from the rest of the country, particularly in the cultivation of wheat, a crop Tibetans did not grow in the past.

The northern part of the Qinghai-Tibet Plateau is called Qiang Tang in Tibetan. It has an even worse climate than elsewhere on the plateau: a severe cold rules supreme here, and even less precipitation befriends the land. Vegetation here, as a result, is even poorer. The vast area is basically uninhabited by people. It is a paradise for local wildlife, however.

Areas in and along the Yarlung Zangbo river valley have a more developed economy than elsewhere in Tibet. Small plains, which are scattered along tributaries of the Yarlung Zangbo river, such as Lhasa, Nianchu and Niyang rivers, are Tibet's granary. Lhasa, the regional capital of Tibet, is located by the side of the Lhasa River, and Xigaze, the second biggest city in Tibet, by the side of the Nianchu River.

The Lifestyle and Customs of Tibetans

Tibetans make up more than 90% of the total population on the Qinghai-Tibet Plateau. Within Tibet, their proportion reaches 96%, with Hans, Mongolians, Moinbas and Lhobas constituting the remaining 4%. According to historical records, the Tibetan ethnic group's place of origin is the valley of the Yalong River, a tributary of the Yarlung

Zangbo River in southern Tibet. In the sixth century, Songzan Gambo, a hero of the Tibetan nationality, unified the whole of Tibet and sent an emissary to Chang'an (present-day Xi'an), capital of the Tang Empire. At his reception by Emperor Taizong, the Tibetan emissary conveyed Songzan Gambo's strong wish to strengthen ties between Tibet and Tang. The Tang emperor also married off Princess Wencheng to Songzan Gambo. When she went to Tibet, Princess Wencheng took from interior China advanced culture and agrotechniques, contributing greatly to cultural and economic development in Tibet.

In the 13th century, when the Mongols ruled China, Tibet formally became part of Chinese territory. In Tibet, the Yuan (Mongol) Dynasty imposed a rule characterized by an integration of religion and politics (that is, joint exercise of power by the nobility and the clergy). This political system continued until the end of the 1950s.

Yaks, unique to the Qinghai-Tibet Plateau, are known as "boats of the highland" for their exceptional mountain-climbing and load-carrying abilities.

Tibetans believe in Mahayana (Greater Vehicle) branch of Buddhism. After its introduction into Tibet in the seventh century, Buddhism, after absorbing certain content of indigenous religions, developed into what is commonly known as "Tibetan Buddhism," which up to now has a history of more than 1,000 years. After the 13th century, owing to vigorous promotions by local rulers, Buddhism gradually flourished, with Buddhist temples and monasteries spread all over Tibet. Almost all Tibetans are pious Buddhist believers.

The Tibetan script is an alphabetic writing with a long history. Tibetan-language Great Buddhist Scriptures (da zang jing, or the Tripitaka), a Buddhist classic, Life of Milha Riba, a Tibetan folk biographical works, and books recording Tibetan medical practices, Tibetan medicines and astronomical observations, are among Tibetan people's great contributions to the cultural development of

Yamzho Yumco Lake in Tibet. The lake abounds in fish and is surrounded by pastureland.

the Chinese nation.

Tibetans are a tenacious, optimistic people with a strong physique. They wear robes and boots and like to deck themselves out with decorative articles. Meat and zanba -- roasted highland barley flour -- are their staple food. Tibetans drink a butter tea three times a day and love a mild alcoholic drink brewed from highland barley. Most Tibetans live in two- or three-storied watchtower-like stone houses with small windows. Unlike Mongolian herdsmen who live in round-shaped yurts, Tibetan herdsmen live in rectangular oxhide tents.

Scripture-chanting lamas

Tibetans are good at singing and dancing. Tibetan songs are melodious and strongly rhythmic; the singing of songs is almost always accompanied by dancing. Tibetan dances are unrestrained and their most popular forms are tida dance (group dancing with emphasis on footwork), guozhuang dance (group dancing along a loop), xianzi dance (group dancing to the accompaniment of a stringed instrument called xianzi).

Among many traditional Tibetan festivals, the better known are the Tibetan New Year's Day, Bathing Festival, Xuedun Festival (also called the Yogurt Festival) observed in pasturelands, and Wangguo (fruit-expecting) Festival observed in farming areas. The first two are common festivals of all Tibetans. Customs on the Tibetan New Year' Day are similar to those on the New Year's Day of the lunar calendar celebrated by the majority of the Chinese people. On the Bathing Festival that falls in early July of the Tibetan calendar, all Tibetans, male and female, old and young, would jump into rivers to cleanse themselves of a year's dirt and pray for good luck in the new year.

Developing the Qaidam Basin

In the northern part of the Qinghai-Tibet Plateau is a relatively low-lying area -- the Qaidam Basin. In the Mongolian language, Qaidam means "salt pond." This is a fitting name since lake basins, salt depressions and swamps are scattered all over the Qaidam Basin. Before the 1950s, the vast area was almost uninhabited.

With extremely rich natural resources, the Qaidam Basin is reputed as a "treasure bowl." In the last four decades, the state has invested heavily in resources prospecting in the basin; land has been reclaimed and farms set up in areas where conditions allow; and a number of large factories have been built in areas with rich mineral resources. Resources development has been accompanied by

Qinghai Lake. The Qinghai Basin centering on the lake is a fine natural pastureland with scattered farming communities.

The Qinghai-Tibet Plateau has rich geothermal energy resources. Picture shows a geothermal field in Tibet's Ngari area.

the construction of roads and railways. Up to now, a basin-wide road network has been in place; and Golmud, an important city in the heart of the Qaidam Basin, is now linked with Xining, the capital of Qinghai Province. The Xining-Golmud Railway is part of a railway that is to extend further to Lhasa, the regional capital of Tibet. The once bleak and desolate Qaidam Basin has been playing an increasingly important role in China's economic life.

In a broad sense, Qaidam includes the Qaidam Basin and the Qinghai Lake Basin.

Qinghai Lake is the largest lake and also the largest salt lake in China. Extending more than 100 km from east to west and over 60 km from north to south, the lake has an area of 4,583 sq. km. The lake is surrounded by mountains but has wide lakeside plains, which, covered with grass, are good pasturelands.

The water in Qinghai Lake has a bluish green

color, hence its name (Qinghai literally means green sea in Chinese). In the lake are two islets, one of which is called the Bird Island, home to hundreds of thousands of spot-headed geese, fish gulls, yellow ducks, Chinese cormorants, brown-headed gulls and black-necked cranes in summer. They make nestles and breed the young on the island until the arrival of winter, when they return to the south. The Bird Island is now a nature reserve.

In recent years, Qinghai Lake has kept shrinking. The Bird Island, which was truly an island before the 1970s, has since 1976 been linked with the lakeside to become rather a peninsula owing to a drop of the lake's water level. It is a pressing task to protect the Bird Island as a nature reserve.

Qaidam abounds in salt, lead-zinc deposits, petroleum and coal. Salt deposits amounting to about 60 billion tons are concentrated in several salt lakes in the basin, ranking first in the country. The salt lakes also contain rich boron, lithium, magnesium and potassium. Sylvite, a source for potash, is produced mainly from the Cha'erhan Salt Pond, the largest of its kind in the Qaidam Basin. The amount of proven sylvite there reaches about 300 million tons, more than 70% of the national total. At present, much salt is produced from the Chaka Salt Pond in the eastern part of Qaidam; and China's biggest potash plant built recently near the Cha'erhan Salt Pond produces 200,000 tons of potash fertilizer a year.

Salt production at Chaka Salt Pond in Qinghai Province

Qinghai Lake's Bird Island

Lead-zinc deposits are located in Xiguangshan in the northeastern part of the Qaidam Basin. Deposits are huge in amount and the ore has a high grade. A mine built there has a capacity to dig and dress one million tons of ore a year.

Petroleum is produced near Lenghu Lake in the western part of the basin. An oil refinery, built in Golmud, has strategic importance: it supplies oil products to Tibet as well as to local customers.

2.4
Beijing, Shanghai and New-Emerging Development Zones

Beijing — China's Political and Cultural Center

Beijing is the capital of the People's Republic of China, China's political and cultural center and a cultural city of great fame in the orient. Located at the northern periphery of the North China Plain, 150 km distant from the Bohai Sea to its southeast, Greater Beijing covers 16,800 sq. km and has

The Forbidden City in Beijing

a population of 12.59 million.

Beijing has a history of 3,000 years. And it has always been an important city in north China. During the period of military confrontation between the Northern Song Dynasty (960-1127) and the Liao Dynasty, Beijing became the secondary capital of the latter established by the Qidans residing normally north of the Great Wall. In the following Jin, Yuan, Ming and Qing dynasties, Beijing consistently served as China's political center. After the founding of the People's Republic of China, Beijing was made capital of the nation.

Beijing has strong flavors of an oriental old capital. The Forbidden City — the imperial palatial complex used by rulers of the Ming and Qing dynasties — is located in the center of the city. Beijing's north-south central axis runs right through the Forbidden City, through the City's front and rear gates. The imperial throne located in the Hall of Great Harmony, the central hall of the City, sits right on this central axis. Other buildings in the City stand symmetrically on both sides

of the axis. Streets and lanes in Beijing run either from east to west or from north to south, in a checkerboard pattern. This architectural layout centering on imperial power is rare anywhere else in the world.

Large numbers of ancient buildings and historical relics have been preserved in Beijing. The Forbidden City, called the Palace Museum now, has been preserved well. It is one of the largest and grandest palatial complexes in the world. The Tiananmen Gate Tower in front of the Forbidden City, formerly the southern gate of the imperial city, is the symbol of Beijing. In front of the Tiananmen Gate Tower is vast Tiananmen Square. In the center of the square stand Monument to the People's Heroes and Mao Zedong Memorial Hall.

The Asian Games Village in Beijing

The Forbidden City is flanked by Zhongshan Park and Working People's Cultural Palace. North of the City, in close proximity, are Jingshan Park and Beihai Park. Together, these form a complete architectural group, allowing viewers to appreciate China's ancient architecture and providing people with a strong reminder of the country's history.

Beijing has a long and rich cultural tradition. It is this ancient city that has fostered Beijing dialect characterized by clear pronunciation of Chinese characters and a pleasing tone; and on the basis of this Beijing dialect has developed putonghua — the common speech of the entire nation. Beijing has given birth to the best-known of Chinese operas — Peking Opera. Beijing's traditional catering trade satisfies people of ethnic minority groups such as Manchus and Mongolians as well as the majority Han Chinese, offering the well-known Peking Duck and Mongolian Hot Pot, for example. Beijing's courtyard houses have a rational layout

The Great Wall, more than 6,300 km long, winds among mountains and across deserts and grasslands in northern China.

and a unique architectural style; lanes (called hutong in Chinese) lined with courtyard houses are filled with human warmth and good neighborliness. All these have a great appeal for tourists. Beijing's traditional craftsmen have superior skills. Their products — cloisonne ware, jade carvings and carpets — enjoy a high reputation on the world market.

Beijing is also China's science and cultural center. The city is home to the country's biggest library — the Beijing Library, the country's biggest sporting facilities, first-rate hospitals, dozens of state-level art organizations, and 120 museums.

Autumn red in Beijing's Fragrant Hills

It is also China's media and publishing center. Concentrated in Beijing are close to 100 institutions of higher learning, including Beijing University and Qinghua University, which enroll foreign as well as Chinese students. The city is home to China's biggest research organizations — Chinese Academy of Sciences and Chinese Academy of Social Sciences, and to most of the more than 100 research institutes under them. The Zhongguanchun area in the northwestern part of Beijing is where talent and technology are concentrated. Located here are Beijing University, Qinghua University and research institutes under the Chinese Academy of Sciences. Recent years have seen a rapid development of a high-tech industry at Zhongguanchun, which as a result has been known as "China's silicon valley."

Beijing has a strong industrial base. Its industrial sector covers mainly iron and steel, coal mining, machine-building, petrochemicals, electronics and textiles. Big enterprises in the city include the Capital Iron & Steel Corp., Jingxi Coal Mine, Yanshan Petrochemical Co. and a Chinese-US joint venture producing Cherokee jeeps. Since the beginning of the 1990s, traditional industries producing iron and steel, chemicals and textiles have been going technology-intensive; at the same time, high- and new-tech industries covering information technology and services, optical-electromechanical integration, bioengineering, new pharmaceuticals and new materials have become focuses of the city's industrial development.

Beijing is China's transportation hub, by road, by rail and by air. Many railways and trunk highways link it with the rest of the country. The Beijing-Tianjin-Tanggu Expressway has cut the time of travel between the Chinese capital and the sea. Beijing's Capital Airport is China's largest, with numerous routes leading to many foreign cities as well as to other parts of China.

Since the implementation of reform and open policies in China, Beijing has been taking on a new look almost on a daily basis. Its Second Ring Road and Third Ring Road, free of traffic lights thanks to flyovers at all intersections, provide unimpeded round-the-city traffic. The rate of home telephone ownership is among the highest in the country. Recent years have seen rapid increases of high-rise buildings as well as public lawns and greenery-

Beijing

Shanghai's Nanjing Road

covered zones in the city. Beijing has "grown taller" and "become more beautiful," people say.

Relevant departments in Beijing have drawn up a long-term development plan for Beijing in the 21st century. Beijing is expected to become even more beautiful in the near future.

Shanghai — China's Economic Center

With a population of 13 million, Shanghai is a world-class metropolis. But the municipality has an area of only 6,340 sq. km. On this limited piece of land, the people of Shanghai have developed their city into China's economic center and No.1 port. Shanghai ranks in the forefront among China's provinces and regions in terms of annual industrial and agricultural output value, export earnings and cargo handling.

Shanghai is located on the southern bank of the Yangtze River at its mouth. The Huangpu River, the Yangtze's last tributary, cuts through the city. Despite being a big port, Shanghai proper is not lapped by sea waves. Downtown Shanghai is more than 20 km distant from Wusong, the gateway to Shanghai from the sea. Docks line the 80km section of the Huangpu in the city. It is the Huangpu River that has made Shanghai a port; and there would not be Shanghai of today without its bustling port.

Shanghai is the cradle of China's modern industry. Following the Opium War of 1840-42, Shanghai was opened as a trading port. With a massive influx of foreign capital, Shanghai quickly developed into the biggest financial center in the Far East. In the meantime, modern textile, machine-building and food-processing industries came into being in the city. Shanghai became a bustling commercial city with a great concentration of traders and shops selling both home-made

Shanghai's Pudong New Area
as viewed from the old city

products and imports. After the founding of New China, Shanghai has always been China's biggest industrial base as well as its biggest tax payer and profit contributor.

Shanghai is China's biggest industrial and commercial city. It has a whole range of heavy and light industries. The iron and steel industry is one of Shanghai's traditional industrial sectors. The Baoshan Iron & Steel Corp. has an important place in the country. The city also has a well-developed petrochemical industry. The Jinshan Petrochemical Corp. located in the southeastern suburbs of Shanghai is one of the nation's largest petrochemical enterprises. The years since the beginning of the 1990s have witnessed a further strengthening of the city's six "pillar" industries: carmaking, telecom equipment manufacturing, iron and steel,

Shanghai's container terminals

petrochemicals and fine chemicals, power equipment and big machinery manufacturing, and consumer electronics and home appliances production. In the meantime, much headway has been made in the development of high- and new-tech industries covering integrated circuits and computers, bioengineering and pharmaceuticals, and new materials.

Shanghai owes its status as the nation's economic center to its superior geographical location: at the mouth of the Yangtze and the central point of China's coastline. The city is linked with interior areas of the country by the Yangtze, with other Chinese port cities by coastal waters, and with the rest of the world by sea. If China's arc-like coastline is compared to a bow, the Yangtze is then an arrow put to the bow. It is by relying on this "arrow" that Shanghai has been serving as a bridge between China and the rest of the world.

Reform and implementation of the open-door policy have instilled new vitality into Shanghai. In recent years, Shanghai's economy has been developing at an ever faster speed. This is particularly true since 1990 when the Chinese government decided to develop Pudong, a Singapore-sized piece of land wedged between Shanghai proper and the East China Sea. Pudong has been intended as a primary destination for foreign investment and Pudong's development aims to speed up development not only in Shanghai but also along the entire Yangtze Valley and the entire country.

Shanghai's "Oriental Pearl" TV Tower

The Bund in Shanghai

Economic development in Shanghai's Pudong New Area has been rapid and robust. A host of foreign businesses, including many well-known multinational corporations, have invested in the area. Numerous domestic enterprises have set up shops in Pudong, too, to engage in all kinds of economic activities. The Lujiazui Financial & Trade Zone in Pudong and the Bund — the time-honored financial street of the old city, facing each other across the Huangpu and linked by a tunnel under the river, have combined to be an integral entity on its way to becoming the busiest business district in China. Pudong's Jinqiao Export Processing Zone features new- and high-tech development and the development of new industries. Its Zhangjiang High-Tech Park is home to many high-tech projects with bioengineering firms having the most prominent place. And its Waigaoqiao Bonded Zone is doing brisk processing-based trade, trade in services and entrepot trade.

The Shanghai municipal government has invested heavily in infrastructure construction for Pudong's development. The newly-built Yangpu and Nanpu bridges span the Huangpu to connect Pudong with the city proper; numerous high-rise buildings have sprung up in Pudong; a new international airport is being built in the area; and the port of Shanghai has increased its cargo handling capacity with the expansion of deep berths.

Shanghai is younger than most Chinese cities. In more than 100 years, Shanghai has developed from a small seaside town into a metropolis with a population of 13 million. In this city, immigrants and their descendants far exceed locals and their descendants in number. Non-locals in Shanghai have come mainly from southern Jiangsu and

Shenzhen at night

northeastern Zhejiang and include a small number of foreign immigrants and their descendants. Exchanges between Shanghai's local and non-local residents over long years have resulted in a local culture unique to Shanghai. The Shanghai dialect has strong elements of dialects prevalent in Jiangsu and Zhejiang, and people's lifestyle in Shanghai is similar to that in the two provinces. Yue Opera and Pingtan performance (storytelling and ballad singing in Suzhou dialect) popular in Shanghai have their origin in Zhejiang and Jiangsu respectively. Under the influence of big, modern industries, Shanghai residents seem to pay greater attention to efficiency, have a shrewder economic eye and put a greater premium on the quality of life, than people elsewhere in China. And, certainly, they are better educated, too.

Sanya at the southern tip of Hainan Island

Special Economic Zones and Open Cities

To promote economic development, the Chinese government began implementing reform and open-door policies after 1978. From 1980, it successively established four special economic zones: Shenzhen, Zhuhai and Shantou in Guangdong Province and Xiamen in Fujian Province. In 1984, the government further opened to foreign investment 14 coastal cities including Dalian and Shanghai. More opening moves were taken later: Hainan was made a province and declared a special economic zone, the biggest among the SEZs; coastal open areas were further expanded, resulting in the following well-known open zones: the Pearl River

Delta, the Yangtze River Delta, the Southern Fujian Zone encompassing the cities of Quanzhou, Zhangzhou and Xiamen, Shandong Peninsula, Liaodong Peninsula, Coastal Hebei and Coastal Guangxi.

In 1990, the Chinese government decided to open Shanghai's Pudong and a number of cities along the Yangtze. This has resulted in a Yangtze Valley Economic Belt with Shanghai's Pudong as its driving force. In 1992, the government decided to open 13 cities and towns along China's border and further opened provincial capitals in interior areas of the country. In addition, a number of bonded zones and economic & technological development zones were established in or near major open cities. Up to now, China's open policy implementation is all-round, multi-tiered and multi-channeled, and open policies are applied in coastal areas, areas along big rivers and borders, and interior areas.

Special Economic Zones

China's five special economic zones are: Shenzhen, Zhuhai, Shantou, Xiamen and Hainan. Shenzhen SEZ, located on the northern shore of the Pearl River Mouth and bordering Kowloon across the Shenzhen River, has an area of 327.5 sq. km. With the Pearl River Delta as its heartland and its close proximity to Hong Kong and Macao, Shenzhen is advantageously located. Since its establishment in 1980 as China's first SEZ, Shenzhen has developed into a big, modern city with an urbanized area of more than 30 sq. km and a population of more than one million. Luhu District bordering Hong Kong is Shenzhen's business area, whose landmark is the 160-meter tall, 53-storied World Trade Center. Main industries in Shenzhen are electronics, machine-building and chemicals. Most factories there are export-oriented, and Chinese-foreign joint ventures make up a high proportion of all industrial enterprises there. The majority of Shenzhen's products are exported, and Shenzhen is one of the biggest foreign exchange earners among China's big cities.

Gulangyu Islet (foreground), part of the city of Xiamen, Fujian Province

Zhuhai SEZ, located on the west shore of the Pearl River Mouth and bordering Macao, covers 121 sq. km in area. Zhuhai has made impressive progress in urban development. Shantou SEZ is divided into two parts: one part covering 22.6 sq. km is located in the eastern suburbs of Shantou; and the other part covering 30 sq. km is located on Guang'ao Peninsula in the southeastern suburbs of Shantou. Xiamen SEZ covering 131 sq. km comprises Xiamen Island and the nearby Gulangyu Islet.

Hainan SEZ consisting of the entire Hainan Island and having an area of 34,000 sq. km, is China's biggest SEZ. In 1992 the central government approved the establishment of a Yangpu Development Zone on Yangpu Peninsula in the northwestern part of Hainan, where economic policies similar to "free port" ones are applied.

Coastal Open Cities and Coastal Open Zones

China's 14 coastal open cities are, from north to south: Dalian, Qinhuangdao, Tianjin, Yantai, Qingdao, Lianyungang, Nantong, Shanghai, Ningbo, Wenzhou, Fuzhou, Guangzhou, Zhangjiang and Beihai. By prioritizing industrial development, overseas investment absorption and export expansion, these cities have achieved remarkable economic results over the years.

The country's five open zones are: Yangtze River Delta, Pearl River Delta, Southern Fujian comprising Quanzhou, Zhangzhou and Xiamen,

Haikou, capital of Hainan Province

Map of China's Special Economic Zones, Development Areas, Bonded Zones and Border Economic Development Areas

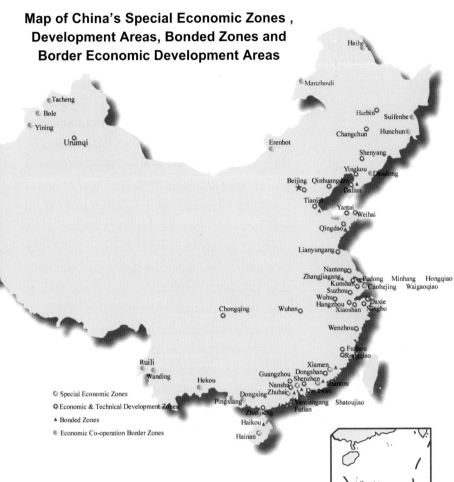

© Special Economic Zones
O Economic & Technical Development Zones
▲ Bonded Zones
◖ Economic Co-operation Border Zones

Shandong Peninsula, and Liaodong Peninsula.

Border Open Cities

Since 1992, the government has opened 13 border cities, namely Hunchun in Jilin, Suifenhe and Heihe in Heilongjiang, Manzhouli and Erlianhot in Inner Mongolia, Tacheng, Bole and Yining in Xinjiang, Hekou, Wanding and Ruili in Yunnan,

Pingxiang and Dongxing in Guangxi, together with all the inland provincial capitals except Lhasa. Open cities along the Yangtze River are: Chongqing, Yueyang in Hunan, Huangshi in Hubei, Jiujiang in Jiangxi and Wuhu in Anhui.

Bonded Zones

To attract more foreign investment, the Chinese government has from 1990 established bonded zones in some open cities. Bonded zones are small enclosed areas that are similar to special zones overseas having "free port" and free trade zone functions. They also have the comprehensive functions of export-oriented processing and foreign trade. Within bonded zones, special tariff policies and special management methods are applied.

At present, there are a total of 15 bonded zones in China. They are: Shanghai Waigaoqiao Bonded Zone, Tianjin Port Bonded Zone, Dalian Bonded Zone, Shenzhen Shatoujiao Bonded Zone, Shenzhen Futian Bonded Zone, Shenzhen Yantian Bonded Zone, Guangzhou Bonded Zone, Zhuhai Bonded Zone, Zhangjiagang Bonded Zone, Haikou Bonded Zone, Qingdao Bonded Zone, Ningbo Bonded Zone, Fuzhou Bonded Zone, Xiamen Xiangyu Bonded Zone and Shantou Bonded Zone.